Principles of Practical Beekeeping

Robert Couston
N.D.B.

Former Specialist Beekeeping Adviser at
The Scottish Colleges of Agriculture.

Past President of The Scottish Beekeeper's Association.

Past Chairman of The Bee Farmer's Association.

Past Member of The Examination Board for
The National Diploma in Beekeeping

Delegate to the International Federation of
Beekeepers' Associations.

Northern Bee Books
1990

First published by the author 1972.
Revised edition published by
Northern Bee Books, 1990
Scout Bottom Farm, Scout Bottom Road,
Mytholmroyd, Hebden Bridge, W. Yorks. HX7 5JS

Copyright © Robert Couston 1990

Printed by Arc & Throstle Press, Todmorden, Lancs.

ISBN 0 907908 48 9

CONTENTS

CONTENTS

Principles of Practical Beekeeping

By Robert Couston, N.D.B.

INTRODUCTION

From the dawn of human history the life of the honey bee has fascinated the intellect of man and from as far back as the days of the Pharoes the bee has played an important role in the economy of civilisation. Throughout the centuries, philosophers and naturalists have unfolded many strange and amazing facts about the bee colony and it may be rather surprising to find that such a small creature has aroused so great an interest that more has been written about the honey bee than any other creature apart from man himself.

The most outstanding discoveries about bees have been made over the last century and as in nearly all spheres of knowledge, the past few decades have seen a tremendous acceleration of scientific advancement and the improvement of practical techniques. The discovery of the significance of the bee dance, modern swarm control methods and the treatment of diseases are but a few examples of progress within a lifetime and the mind reels at the thought of newer horizons which may open up by the aid of further scientific achievements.

These achievements, however, have generally long-reaching implications which may not take on a practical complexion until this present generation has long since departed, yet over the past 20 years much of the technique of apiculture has radically changed. Speedy transport, new materials, modern methods of agriculture and horticulture and a changing pattern of ways of living all present a challenge to the beekeeper who must ever be ready to adapt his methods and equipment if opportunity to the best advantage has to be grasped.

It is with pride, tinged with a little sadness, that we reflect on the quiet, unhurried charm with which the craftsman of yesteryear lovingly devoted himself to his task. The coppersmith fashioning an exquisitely wrought vessel, his hammer tapping the exact spot required, each blow so carefully measured and each design endeavouring to better the previous one. The fisherman contemplating how he could most assiduously contrive to mend a broken net, not just to effect a repair, but to feel the twine run through his palms and to savour the sensation of pulling the knots true and tight. The ploughman combing the tresses of a field, squinting critically down the furrows and in spite of aching muscles, imparting unspoken satisfaction to his horses. An elderly beekeeper, on a balmy July day, sitting in a wicker chair under an overgrown rose and ivy-clad, shaded bower, his eyes feasting on the river sparkling its way down the valley and on the tall mountain scenery beyond, a corn cob pipe on his lap and a stone flagon of cider, covered with a wet white cloth to keep it cool, at his side. A few steps away the humming of bees fills the air with drowsy melody, broken perhaps by the louder droning of an emerging swarm. A gentle smile, a lifting of the flagon to let some refreshing liquid trickle down the throat and once the airily circling bees drop to a cluster, a mellow and sweet-smelling straw skep is placed reverently over them. Squatting at a hive entrance watching the bright blobs of pollen dancing into the darkness, each bee scurrying like a fussy little man dressed in gaudily-coloured breeches - what would the distraught worker in factory and office of today give for a few hours of such bliss?

Alas the bulldozer of progress has flattened our paths into well-defined channels and the full-time luxury of such an exquisite pastime is not for most of us. Although we cannot perhaps sit all day under our shady bower listening to the gentle winging of our bees, and although we may be compelled to adopt many unromantic ideas, every beekeeper, no matter how small or large, can always devote a little time to stand and stare.

The object of this book is not to enlarge on the many such pleasurable moments afforded to every beekeeper, nor is any originality or all aspects of apiculture claimed or covered, but an attempt has been made to amplify some of the underlying principles necessary for the production of surplus honey and for the beekeeper to maintain the wellbeing of his charges.

The writer has been especially privileged in forming many friendships with beekeepers from vastly differing circumstances, who not only shared their knowledge of successes, but more important, gave unstintingly of their experiences of trials and setbacks. It is mainly on this latter information that much of the contents is based and it is to these good people that this book is respectfully dedicated.

Special thanks are due to Mr Donald Robertson, who assisted in the photography and who was responsible for many of the close-up studies, to Mrs Doris Cartwright, who assisted in the script composition, to the Technical Visual Aids Branch of the Ministry of Agriculture for permission to reproduce a selection of their prints which are hereby stated to be Crown Copyright, to the Editor of *"The Scottish Beekeeper"* and the printers for their help and advice and to all others who kindly gave advice and permission to use their material.

To avoid frequent reference, a reader not familiar with beekeeping terminology is advised to study the glossary of terms before perusing the material in this book.

Preface To The Second Edition

Twenty years have elapsed since "Principles of Practical Beekeeping" commenced to be published in January 1968 as a serial in The Scottish Beekeepers' magazine. It was published as a book in 1972 which has since sold 10,000 copies.

The book was also edited and translated into Swedish by Nils Carlsson who modified the information to suit conditions in Scandinavia but the original illustrations were retained. This publication came out in 1976.

Over two decades ago, the author was witnessing the changing Agricultural pattern throughout Europe and other overseas countries, but few could have realised the rate of acceleration and degree of impact which this would have on beekeeping in the British Isles since the United Kingdom became a member of the European Economic Community.

The period after the First World War was the halcyon days for beekeeping in Britain, and this profitable era lasted through to the second World War and for a few decades after it. Because food was scarce - even rationed for several years, beekeepers had no difficulty in obtaining satisfactory prices for their products and commercial-beekeeping was a profitable pursuit.

With the expansion of importations, first from some Commonwealth Countries, mainly Canada, Australia and New Zealand, then a gathering flood of cheap honey from other overseas countries such as Argentina, China, Mexico, and Romania, the profitable marketing of extracted home-produced honey has become increasingly difficult.

Many of the commercial operators who were household-names in the British beekeeping world in the late nineteen-forties, turned to packing and distributing imported-honey for their livelihood. Most of the commercial honey-producers still operating in the South, rely to a great extent on income derived from pollination contracts.

There is however scope for the part-time operator who is willing to practise migratory beekeeping and aim to make the enterprise profitable by selective marketing. In a Supermarket, the housewife may be willing to pay a bit more for a superior, home-produced jar of honey but not double or treble the price asked for a jar of "Blended Imported".

Since the nineteen-fifties when the emphasis was on the production of extracted-honey, to the exclusion of comb-honey which was more difficult to produce and for which no premium prices were offered, the wheel has turned a full circle. Certain home-produced honeys lend themselves ideally for the production of comb in different forms of packaging and these have an added attraction in the "up-market" retail trade outlets.

For the hobbiest beekeeper with only two or three hives, there might not be a high financial gain but the aesthetic quality and pleasure of providing one's relations and friends with a carefully prepared and attractive item for the table, would be difficult to measure.

The measurements in this edition are mainly in Imperial units because most beekeeping equipment and recipes are still quoted in this form. To convert inches to centimetres multiply by 2.54; to convert pints to litres multiply by 0.5682; and to convert pounds to kilograms, multiply by 0.4536.

GLOSSARY OF BEEKEEPING TERMS

Apiary	A place where bees are kept.
Bee Space or Bee Way	A space between ¼-⅜ inch which bees leave open. In moveable frame hives such a space is created between and at the ends of combs and hive compartments.
Brace Comb	Small areas of comb built by bees in unwanted positions.
Brood	A term applied to the larvae (unsealed brood) and pupae (sealed brood) in a bee colony.
Brood Chamber or Brood Box	The compartment in a hive reserved for the rearing of brood.
Brood Nest	The area of comb used by bees for the rearing of brood.
Cast	A secondary swarm of bees headed by a virgin queen.
Clearing Board	A framed board into which non-returnable traps are inserted between honey supers and brood chamber to remove bees from honey.
Colony	The inmates of a hive and their comb.
Comb	Haxagonal cells built of bees' wax. Also used to describe the complete wooden framed cell areas of comb which make up the interior of a hive.
Cover Board or Crown Board	A framed board used to cover the topmost compartment in a hive.
Crate	A wooden box to contain sections in a hive.
Divider	Flat, wooden, metal or plastic sheet inserted between rows of sections to keep them even and prevent joining together.
Drawn Comb	Combs of completed cells built on wax foundation by bees.
Dummy Board	A wooden board fitting the interior of a hive compartment, parallel to the combs, to fill up an end space. Its removal allows space for manipulating combs. Not now in common use.
Foundation	Thin sheets of bees' wax embossed on both sides with cell bases. These are fitted into wooden frames and when introduced to a colony are built into combs.
Frame	A wooden structure to contain foundation and latterly comb, which fits into a hive compartment to leave a bee space at either end.
"Green" Honey	Newly-gathered nectar or honey in open cells which has not been completely processed by bees and from which the excess moisture has not evaporated.
Hive	A wooden box designed to house bees. Sometimes erroneously used to describe a stock of bees.
Hive Tool	A metal instrument used to prise apart hive compartments and to scrape propolis and brace comb from unwanted areas.
Nucleus (pl. Nuclei)	A small colony of bees on combs.
Package	A cluster of bees shaken into a cage with a queen, but without combs.
Queen Excluder	A device made of slotted zinc or framed wire spaced wide enough to allow worker bees through, but narrow enough to exclude a queen bee. Used to confine a queen in a brood chamber of a hive.
Ripener	A tall metal tank with a strainer at the top and a honey tap at the bottom. Used for settling and the temporary storage of honey after extraction. It does not ripen honey.
Robbing	When a colony is weak other bees in the vicinity may attack it and carry the stored honey back to their own hives.
Rollers	Stout cloth affixed to two cylindrical wooden battens the width of a hive. Used in controlling bees when handling.
Section	A small wooden frame to contain foundation and latterly honey comb. Generally 4¼ inches square.
Skep	An old-fashioned hive made of plaited straw. Now employed for catching swarms.
Smoker	A device consisting of a bellows and a metal barrel in which material is burned to produce smoke for subduing bees.
Stock	Bees, combs and stores complete in a bee hive.
Stores	Food, both pollen and honey, in a stock. Generally refers to that stored in the brood chambers.
Strainer	A funnel-shaped, metal container with a fine mesh bottom used for straining honey into a "ripener".
Super	Hive compartment, usually shallow, with foundation or comb, used for storing honey when on a hive.
Supering	The act of adding supers to stocks.
Swarm	Bees with a queen which have left their hive.
Veil	Cloth or plastic netting worn with a hat to protect the face from bee stings.

1

SOME USEFUL TEMPERATURES

Fahrenheit		Celcius
235®	Boiling point of bee candy solution (5lbs (2.71 kg) sugar to 1 pint (.57 litres) water) (use candy thermometer only)	112.8®
185®	Beeswax starts to discolour when subjected to dry heat.	85®
150®	Caramelisation of ling heather honey may occur depending on length of time	65.5®
146®	Average melting point of beeswax but can vary according to composition	63.6®
145®	Heating for 30 minutes destroys yeasts to prevent fermentation but can impair some honeys.	62.8®
140®	Maximum for warm water to flush and dissolve honey in machines. Microwave treatment to reliquify granulated honey in jars.	60®
130®	Separating and melting granulated honey from cappings 1-2 days.	54○
122®	Honey viscosity suitable for pumping and filtering. Small granules melt 8-16 hours.	50®
120®	Stirring for cooled bee-candy solution.	48.9®
104®	Maximum for spinning cappings in centrifuge.	40®
90®	Pre-heating heather and oil-seed rape honey combs prior to extracting (36 hours +)	32®
80®	Pre-heating blossom honey combs prior to extracting (12 hours +)	26.7®
75®	Introducing seeding for granulating honey (5%-10% seed). Introducing yeast cultures to mead mixtures.	23.9®
57®	Encourages rapid granulation.	13.9®
50®	Storage of honey in bulk or in jars	10®

Chapter I.

THE LIFE OF THE BEE COLONY

There are three types of insect found in a bee-colony during the active season. Two of them are females divided into the queen and worker caste, the other is a male, commonly called a drone bee. *(Fig.1.)*

The Queen.

The name "queen bee" implies that she is some form of ruler, whereas her mission in life is solely that of egg laying. The queen does not tend her young; nevertheless, she is the mother of the bee colony, all the inmates springing from the fruits of her ovaries. The queen starts her active life after hatching during the summer months, and after leading a virginal life of anything from a few days to six weeks, she emerges from the hive for her nuptial flights.

Once it was supposed that when a queen flew thus, she was seized and mated while on the wing by the strongest and swiftest drone bee in the vicinity and that this romantic, if somewhat hasty, union occurred only once. It is now generally agreed that a queen often makes several mating flights within a period of a few days, returning to the hive each time with the dismembered genitalia of her latest mate adhering to her body.

During or immediately following the mating, the male element, or sperms, from the drone travels into a receptacle called the spermatheca, where it mingles with a fluid medium which preserves and nourishes it. Here it is stored during the queen's useful life. *(Fig.3)*. Should adverse weather conditions, or other mischance, prevent the queen from mating within six weeks from time of hatching, the fluid medium in the spermatheca could become unsuitable for the retention of sperms, and would result in her inability to lay fertilised eggs. When proper mating does occur, the queen then remains in the hive and commences egg laying within a few days.

During the queen's virginal life, the worker bees pay scant attention to her, but once egg laying commences, she is tended and fed by a retinue of workers. Such a mated or "fertile" queen attracts great attention in the hive and the difference in behaviour of the worker bees to such a queen distinguishes her from a virgin queen.

In small nuclei, or in mating boxes, there is frequently a shortage of young bees and in such circumstances a newly-mated queen often lays several eggs in one cell. This condition may also be seen where a young queen has started to lay in a colony which has been queenless for some time. Such behaviour is often confused with that of "laying workers," but within a few days the normal egg-laying pattern of one egg in one cell commences *(Fig.2)*.

Queens have been observed issuing from the hive in early summer for a short flight, but such behaviour does not appear to be significant, nor is it common. Normally a queen remains in the hive after commencing to lay and does not venture from it until and unless the colony swarms.

The duration of a queen bee's life is determined largely by the amount of energy expended; thus, a queen restricted to a small colony for breeding purposes may live for as long as five years, whereas the same queen, used to head a strong honey-gathering stock, would probably end her useful life within three years. In practical beekeeping, re-queening is generally carried out every second year.

Under natural conditions, new queens are reared prior to swarming, but occasionally, when an old queen shows signs of failing, the colony will set about superseding her by rearing one or more young queens. One of these will eventually mate and become the new mother of the colony.

The Worker

The worker bee, as the name implies, performs the many duties required in the running of the colony. Her body is so adapted for specialised tasks that she is virtually a flying tool-kit, each instrument beautifully modelled and positioned for maximum efficiency. To examine the functions of a worker bee, let us follow one of those selfless little insects through her short but varied life.

Newly issued from her cell, the softness of her hair and chitinous outer skeleton give her a downy appearance *(Fig.6)*. Five days or so later, this outer covering hardens and the soft hair stiffens into numerous bristles. At first she is a little unsteady on her legs and after emerging from her cell, will seek a drop of food from one of her older sisters. This food is transferred via their complicated mouth parts.

Within a day or two our baby bee becomes steady on her legs and sets-to, cleaning out the cells newly-vacated by her younger sisters, carefully varnishing the interiors with a mixture of propolis and saliva *(Fig.4)*. Such prepared cells are those in which the queen bee will lay her eggs after inspection. These cells have a highly-polished appearance and their presence in a colony which has had no laying queen for some time may indicate that a queen is about to commence laying, even although there is no evidence of eggs or larvae.

Between three and six days old, the worker bee acts as nursemaid to the older larvae, feeding them with a mixture of diluted honey and pollen, then, as the brood food glands develop in her head, she turns her attention to the very young larvae, feeding them on the powerful hormone food known as Brood Food or Royal Jelly. Thus it may be said that the brood food-secreting period lasts from the fifth or sixth days of the adult bee to the thirteenth day, a period of approximately eight days. During this stage she also carries out the duties of a house bee, storing and packing both pollen and nectar brought in from the field by her older flying sisters.

The eighteenth day of her adult life finds her still mainly confined to the hive, apart from short orientation flights, which are made to strengthen the wing muscles and which help in fixing the location of the hive. Wax secreting and building, cleaning out debris from the hive and acting as a fanner at the hive entrance are other duties which may occupy the remainder of her time during this period.

In order to secrete wax, a number of bees congregate to form a compact cluster and a high temperature is maintained. A considerable amount of honey is consumed beforehand and is converted to beeswax by a chemical process in the body. This wax is secreted in the form of tiny scales from eight glandular orifices situated in the lower part of the abdomen. These scales are then transferred to the mouth where they are rendered into a plastic state before being moulded into the familiar hexagonal-shaped cells.

Fanning bees maintain a through-current of air in the hive and are especially active during hot weather. The efficiency of this ventilation is demonstrated after a heavy gathering of nectar, when excess moisture is evaporated and expelled. Thereafter it condenses and small rivulets of water may be seen trickling from the hive entrance. Fanning bees expose a small white scent gland, called the Nasenoff organ, which is situated at the tip of the abdomen *(Fig. 93)*. The scent attracts flying bees to the area and young bees especially are less likely to stray when returning from their orientation flights due to this scent beacon.

QUEEN - WORKER - DRONE

Fig. 1. Castes of the honey bee
(Photo MAFF)

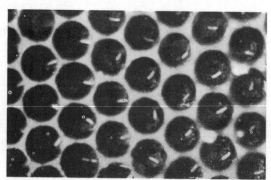

Fig. 2. Eggs in worker cells.

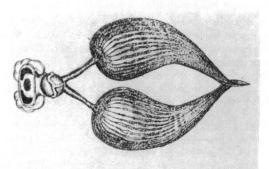

Fig. 3. Diagram of queen's reproductive system (Photo MAFF)

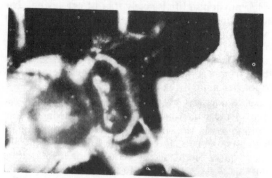

Fig. 4. Young worker bee cleaning out and "varnishing" interior of brood cell.

Fig. 5. Worker brood in various stages including eggs.

Fig. 6. Young worker bees emerging from cells—termed hatching brood.

Fig. 7. Honey and pollen cells.

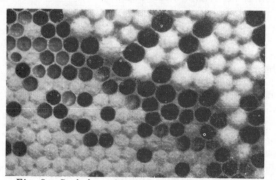

Fig. 8. Sealed worker and drone brood cells.

4

After eighteen days or so of adult life our bee now graduates to a forager, flying from the hive to gather the raw materials necessary for the existence of the colony. These are water, pollen, propolis and nectar, which are usually gathered in that order according to her age.

Water is required for the dilution of honey, particularly in the spring months when only honey carried over from the previous season is available in the hive for feeding larvae. Water, which is carried in the bee's honey sac, is also gathered during hot weather and is stored in and around the brood nest. By process of evaporation, latent heat is utilised and the temperature of the hive is controlled.

Pollen is the male fertilising agent of flowers and supplies the protein diet necessary for the development of the bee larvae. It is gathered and packed into the pollen baskets of the forager bee; two flat indentations on its rear legs, surrounded by stiff bristles *(Fig.12)*. Returning to the hive, the pollen forager deposits its load in cells immediately surrounding the brood area, where it is broken down and carefully packed by house bees. Some of this pollen may be used immediately for feeding larvae *(Fig.7)*. When it is packed for storage, pollen is first of all covered with a film of honey before being sealed over with a wax capping. This honey seal is air-tight and effectively prevents deterioration.

Young foragers of about the pollen-gathering stage may act as guard bees at the entrance and extremities of the hive and it is their duty to repel strange bees, or other invaders, including the beekeeper, from forcing an entry.

Propolis is a gum-like substance exuded from many varieties of buds, leaves and barks while a substance akin to it is secreted by worker bees after the digestion of pollen. True propolis is carried back to the hive in the pollen baskets and used for sealing crevices whereas that secreted by bees is employed in varnishing the interior of the hive to effect a smooth and vermin-free surface and, as mentioned, to coat the inside of cells used for brood rearing. Some strains of bees, particularly those with Caucasian ancestry, often construct a barrier of propolis at the hive entrance *(Fig.54)*.

Nectar, a thin, watery substance containing complex sugar, is secreted by many plants and trees at different times of the year under various weather and soil conditions. Nectar is sucked up from the nectary of the flower through the bee's mouth parts and is carried in the honeysac located at the forepart of the abdomen. Here an organ called the proventriculus filters out much of the foreign matter and the nectar is mixed with digestive juices.

On returning to the hive, the nectar-forager regurgitates its load directly into a cell or to a house bee again via the mouth parts. It is then manipulated in the mouths of other bees before final storage in a honey-cell. More digestive enzymes are added at each stage and this has the effect of breaking down the complex sugar content of the nectar to simple sugars, mainly dextrose (glucose) and levulose (fructose). The excess moisture is evaporated-off by the hive ventilation and a thick viscous product results - honey.

Returning scout foragers impart information on the distance and direction of a food source to other bees by means of a dance within the hive, at the same time distributing a sample of the secured food. Observation of such behaviour is one of the many fascinatng aspects afforded to the beekeeper or naturalist.

Although the pattern of duties is largely determined by the bee's age, the routine is extremely flexible. For instance, if a sharp nectar flow occurred after a prolonged dearth, many bees would omit water and pollen gathering to take full advantage of the flow. Conversely, bees hatched in the autumn retard their nursing capabilities until the following spring.

Our little bee's life is now drawing to a close. After about six weeks of active adult life in the summer months, waste products accumulate in her body. With frayed wings and worn out organs she perishes, usually at some distance away from her hive. Worker bees hatched in the autumn, however, have less work to perform, as they pass the winter in a state of semi-torpor and may live for over six months. Like the queen bee, their span of life is determined by the energy expended.

The Drone Bee

The drone is the male honey bee and is probably the most specialised insect in the bee colony. He has no built-in tool kit with which to work and apart from helping to generate heat and thereby assisting to keep the brood warm, has no outward concern in the managing of the hive. His sole function is that of being in a position to mate with a queen bee.

In an average-sized colony there may be several hundred or even thousand drones from April to August. One might wonder at this seemingly excessive number of non-productive drones being tolerated, but it is surely Nature's wisdom in ensuring that a queen bee on her mating flight does not have to face the hazards of a lengthy absence from the safety of her home before meeting a partner. Thus the security of the most precious member of the community is safeguarded at the expense of many other lives.

During suitable weather, drones leave their hives and fly to pre-selected spots known as "Drone assemblies" or "Drone congregations". These spots may be close to their apiaries or a few miles distant and are generally sited above a depression between two rising stretches of ground where thermal air-currents push upward. At such spots, an assembly of drones may often be heard, sounding like a small swarm from a bee-colony, but as the circling flight path is usually above thirty metres, binoculars are required to see them.

When mating occurs, the drone not only gives the queen his passionate embrace, but also his life. The male organs are detached during coupling, the drone dying almost immediately and the queen returns to her hive with the proof of her mating firmly implanted in her body.

Towards the end of the summer, rearing and mating of queens usually ceases and as a colony has no further use for its now redundant residents, the workers turn upon the drones in fury. First they gnaw their wing bases so they are unable to fly, then forcibly eject them from their home, where they quickly perish from cold.

When a colony has no mated queen present in the autumn, it will frequently retain its drones as well as fugitive drones from other hives, no doubt in the hope that a new queen could be raised or a present virgin queen be mated. Such attempts seldom meet with success, but a useful clue is given to the beekeeper. In an apiary at this time, if one hive has drones flying from it several weeks after the others have cast their drones, it is an indication that all is not well within and an examination should be made forthwith.

Origin of the Worker Bee

How are these three different types of insect created in a bee colony?

Let us examine the development of the worker bee first. The queen bee deposits a fertilised egg in an ordinary worker cell where it stands upright, parallel to the sides and attached to the cell base for the first day. As the embryo develops, the egg heels over at an angle of about 45 degrees on the second day and on the third day, lies flat on the base of the cell before hatching into a small larva.

The tiny larva is now attended by nurse bees, which secrete and feed their charges with brood food or Royal Jelly. It is placed all around and in direct contact with the body of the larva. This rich, hormone feeding is given for thirty-six hours, after which time the larva is gradually weaned and a mixture of diluted honey and pollen is added to the diet. The feeding of Royal Jelly is terminated on the third day of the worker larva's life, honey and pollen only being given thenceforth.

The larva grows at a tremendous pace so that after six days from hatching it almost completely fills the cell *(Fig. 9)*. At this stage it spins a cocoon while adult bees seal the top of the cell with a porous capping. The larva gradually changes its form as pupation takes place, then on the twenty-first day from the time the egg was laid, the imago, or mature insect, commences to gnaw at the capping and emerges to take up its duties within the hive *(Fig. 10)*.

Origin of the Queen Bee

Queen bees are reared under various impulses. Queen cell cups, which resemble acorn cups in size, are mainly constructed near the centre of the brood nest. Again a fertilised egg is deposited in the cell, which hatches in three days' time. Like the worker larva, the queen larva is fed on Royal Jelly, but instead of being weaned after thirty-six hours, it is lavishly supplied with the powerful hormone food throughout its larval life. This specialised feeding affects the development of the larva, transforming it into a mature female bee, or queen, unlike the worker, which is an immature female.

The queen cell differs in construction from that of the worker. It is larger and extends downwards, thus the occupant develops head downwards instead of on its back *(Fig. 11)*. As before, the cell is sealed over on the ninth day from when the egg was laid, the queen larva spinning her cocoon simultaneously. The difference in feeding also accelerates the rate of growth and the queen emerges from her cell fifteen to sixteen days after the egg was laid.

Origin of the Drone Bee

To understand the origin of the drone bee it is necessary to examine the functioning of the queen bee's reproductive system and to know what is meant by parthenogenesis. In simple language, parthenogenesis could be construed to mean the development of an organism from an unfertilised egg. To explain, let us imagine a poultry yard! It is possible to keep a number of hens which will lay eggs to provide the table with a valuable and nutritius form of food, but these eggs will never hatch into chickens unless a cockerel was present to supply the necessary male element. With some insects, however, the curious phenomenon occurs where the female can lay eggs, and without contact with a male, these eggs develop and hatch out. With the bee, such eggs develop into the male bee of the species, otherwise the drone.

It follows, therefore, that the queen bee can lay either fertilised eggs which hatch into workers, or with the special feeding of Royal Jelly, into queens: or unfertilised eggs which hatch into drones.

To illustrate this point, let us examine an old theory on what happens when a mated queen lays her eggs in the different types of cells. The queen's long, tapering abdomen reaches to the base of the cells and in the case of the worker and queen cells, muscles surrounding the entrance to the spermatheca are relaxed and sperms retained there since mating are allowed access to the egg as it passes down the vagina. The sperms enter the eggs and thus fertilised eggs are laid in both the worker and queen cells.

When a mated queen lays in a drone cell, which is wider or deeper than that of the worker or queen, the muscles surrounding the spermatheca are contracted, effectively excluding access of the sperms. Thus the egg is laid without contact with the male element. An unfertilised egg is, therefore, deposited in the drone cell.

More recent investigations have proved that all eggs laid by a fertile queen receive a supply of sperm when laid and that it is the worker bees who determine the sex of the larvae by removing the sperms or by manipulating the micropyle of the egg.

Development of the drone larva is practically the same as that of the worker. It is an egg for three days and on hatching, is fed in much the same way. The cell is sealed over on the eleventh day, but the capping differs in appearance from that of the worker, being larger and having a bullet-shaped top *(Fig. 8)*. Pupation takes longer than in the case of the queen and the worker, the adult insect not emerging until twenty-four days after the egg was laid.

Drone Breeding Queen

It sometimes happens that a queen, whether through old age, damage to her laying mechanism, or improper mating, has the supply of male sperms either cut off or exhausted and as a result is incapable of laying fertilised eggs. These unfertilised eggs can only develop into drone bees no matter what type of cell they are laid in. Such a queen is termed a "drone breeder" and is easily recognised by the pattern of her laying. The eggs she lays in worker cells develop, but are reared for what they are - drones - and when they are sealed over, the cappings are of the characteristic raised-dome shape *(Fig. 13)*. At the egg and larval stage there is little to distinguish them from worker larvae, as the eggs are laid on the base of the cells in the normal position by the queen *(Fig. 14)*.

If the colony is to survive, such a queen must be replaced.

Laying Workers

When a hive has been queenless for some time, some of the worker bees may attempt the duties of egg laying. It will be remembered that the worker bee is a female, though an undeveloped one, and possesses ovaries which can, under these circumstances, produce eggs. The worker, however, is not capable of being mated. Therefore, the eggs cannot be fertilised and only drones can be produced *(Fig.15)*.

The difference between the work of a drone-breeding queen and that of laying workers can be noted by observing the positions of the eggs in the cells. The worker's shorter abdomen cannot reach to the base of the cells and the eggs are deposited on the cell walls. In addition, the workers, lacking the inherent behaviour of the queen, who generally lays one egg in each cell, often lay a number of eggs in the one cell *(Fig. 16)*. Unfortunately, it is not within the scope of this book to consider all the vastly interestng details of the life of the honey bee - many excellent books have already been written on the subject and should be studied by every beekeeper, but it is hoped that this chapter has cut a useful swath into the field of such knowledge and will serve as a broad guide for the purposes of practical beekeeping.

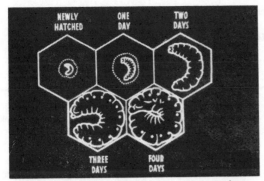

Fig. 9. Diagram of Development of worker bee throughout larval stages (Photo MAFF)

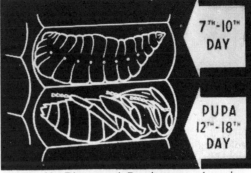

Fig. 10. Diagram of Development of worker bee from larval to pupal stage (Photo MAFF)

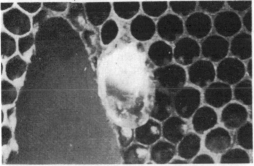

Fig. 11. Queen cell with side removed showing royal jelly.

Fig. 12. Worker bee with filled pollen basket.

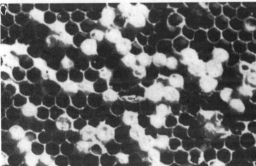

Fig. 13. Work of "drone breeding" queen. Cells are worker cells but have drone-type cappings.

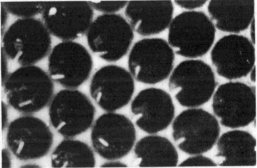

Fig. 14. Eggs laid in worker cells by "drone breeding" queen, showing regular pattern, one egg in each cell and eggs at base of cell.

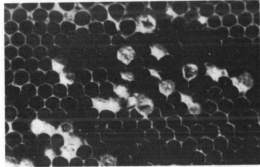

Fig. 15. Work of "laying workers." Again, worker cells with drone cappings.

Fig. 16. Eggs laid in worker cells by "laying workers." Several eggs in each cell and eggs scattered about sides of cells.

Chapter II.

FACTORS AFFECTING HONEY PRODUCTION

Although bees are occasionally kept merely to amuse or be a constant source of wonder to their owners, the majority of beekeepers apply their art, apart from the most interesting and pleasant past-time it affords, in the hope of securing surplus honey. To this end, the many factors which have to be considered can be classified into three main groups. They are, weather, locality and bees.

Weather

Weather, as yet, cannot be controlled and so can be dismissed with these few lines. One point to note is the mistaken impression a beginner may have that hot, dry, sunny days are always ideal for the gathering of nectar. The majority of plants and trees require humidity both to secrete and to retain nectar. Frequently bees are seen to gather much nectar during dull, overcast weather, providing the temperature is high, whereas on warm, sunny days, bees often linger about the hive entrances and do little foraging. In some localities, much of the nectar brought to a hive is gathered in the early morning and in the evening when the dew points are at their highest levels. The heat of the sun and the influence of drying winds throughout the day often dries out moisture in the air and in the nectaries of the flowers.

Heavy rain, thunder storms and high winds all prevent foragers from flying. In addition, heavy rain tends to wash away the formed nectar from many types of flowers.

Locality

Locality is a factor which can be governed sometimes only to a limited extent and fortunate indeed is the beekeeper situated permanently in a favoured locality. Those not so favoured must resort to migratory beekeeping if a creditable honey surplus is to be obtained.

With the best will in the world, bees cannot make honey if raw material in the form of nectar is not available. In desert areas the temperature and humidity at times may be ideal. Place strong stocks of bees there and they would soon starve to death. Sand does not secrete nectar, nor, unfortunately, do many species of vegetation. Therefore, when selecting beekeeping locality, the proper foraging vegetation must be considered.

What plants or trees constitute suitable bee foraging? Many sources of beekeeping information give a comprehensive list of nectar and pollen-producing vegetation, all of which is invaluable knowledge, but what is often missed is the fact that these sources vary tremendously according to species, climate soil conditions and surrounding terrain. Many species of plants do secrete nectar but are so sparsely distributed in some localities and the amount gathered by bees so little, that although useful, do not result in a large honey yield.

A further point to consider is the tendency of many sources to yield only occasionally. In one area at least, the horsechestnut illustrates this point rather well. Beekeepers in the East of Scotland had viewed with some scepticism the informaion that this tree was a good source of nectar, as bees had never been observed to derive much benefit from it over a period of at least 15 years. During the erly summer of 1956, foraging bees deserted the more generally reliable sycamore trees and brought in a very creditable surplus from the chestnut blossom. Since then, at time of writing, there has been no return from this source.

Keeping this in view, it would be unwise for a beekeeper to place his hopes for a honey harvest from such a source, simply because it yielded once in thirty years.

It is not enough to know that there are several nectar secreting sources in the vicinity. Every county in the United Kingdom, every parish, yes, even every apiary site in the country, differs in some way from all others and the beekeeper who would secure a surplus honey crop must ever bear this in mind.

There are a number of known major nectar sources, but even they vary much from place to place, although they form a framework on which foraging information can be built. The following remarks concerning nectar sources apply only to the East of Scotland and it must be appreciated that they do not necessarily apply elsewhere in these Islands. In fact, the reverse is often the case in Southern counties.

Nectar Sources

In early spring there are a few plants and trees which are invaluable sources of pollen, although yielding little or no nectar. These include snowdrop, aconite, butterbur, gorse, elm, willow, flowering currant, wild hyacinth (bluebell), gean, fruit blossom and dandelion. All are useful, but with the exception of gean and fruit blossom in Southern regions, cannot generally be termed major nectar sources.

The much-vaunted hawthorn with its richly-coloured and delightfully-scented honey, does yield well at times South of the Forth Valley, but does not live up to its reputation further North. There, although bees are frequently seen working on it, no evidence of nectar in quantity has been observed in the hives for many years.

The Norwegian maple, regrettably very sparsely distributed and the sycamore with its characteristic, dark green, dense honey, are perhaps the earliest reasonably reliable nectar sources and in some East coastal districts, contribute largely to the year's crop. The fickle chestnut and in some hilly districts, the blaeberry, can on occasion provide a modest crop.

Older sources of beekeeping information in Britain frequently referred to a spell in the active season known as the "June gap". This was a period of nectar-dearth lasting about three weeks, which commenced with the termination of early nectar-flows such as from sycamore, and lasted until the main clover-flow started. This often resulted in a check to colony-development or increaed incidents of swarming behaviour. Many authors-of-the-day advocated feeding colonies with thin sugar-syrup to alleviate this condition.

In the East of Scotland, beekeepers welcomed the month of June as one of the most profitable in the season because of the extensive growing of cultivated raspberries. Depending on the season and on the variety of cane, the raspberry-plants blossom from two to four weeks any time from the last days in May until the first week in July - a fair time to expect reasonable weather for nectar secretion and gathering. The flower is frequently worked by bees during mild rain, providing the temperature is fairly high, as unlike some other flowers, the drooping leaves and petals protect the secreted nectar from being washed out.

Raspberry honey in its fluid state appears very thin but this is due to its high dextrose-sugar content - actually this honey has a very low percentage of water. The Raspberry flow is unsurpassed for the "drawing-out" of comb. Such combs however should be extracted and not sold as comb-honey. Because of its property, this honey is liable to fairly-quick

8

crystallisation, but when suitably treated, results in a creamed or granulated product of the highest quality.

Since the mid-nineteen seventies in England and the early eighties in Scotland, there has been an explosion in the growing of oil-seed rape (OSR). This has had a tremendous impact on traditional methods of honey-production and marketing. There are many varieties of this crop but basically they can be classified into two groups - those which are sown in Autumn and flower in April/May, and those which are sown in Spring and flower in June/July. There is therefore a very long period during which bees may gather nectar and pollen from these sources.

This extensive cultivation of oil-seed rape has brought some very mixed blessings to beekeeping in these islands. Certainly the introduction of this crop to districts which were previously devoid of major nectar-sources has allowed the successful management of medium-sized apiaries there, but in other areas which relied on more traditional foraging, the presence of OSR has caused severe problems.

The difficulties arise because of the rapid granulating property of OSR honey. Large and medium-scale beekeepers must be prepared to remove and extract combs as soon as the honey in them is ripe - sometimes this can be a weekly operation, or else use specialised pulverising and centrifuging machinery, coupled to carefully-controlled heating-techniques which can deal with the crop en masse even when granulated, later in the season.

The presence of even a small amount of OSR honey in stocks can cause problems. Bees move honey around within the hives - sometimes from the brood-chambers into honey-supers and this rapid-granulating honey may find its way into honey-crops later in the season. This can make extracting much more difficult and could ruin what would otherwise be excellent samples of comb-honey.

The small beekeeper in particular, should aim to keep separate sets of combs for use only for OSR and not be tempted to allow part-filled combs to be "finished-off" on later crops.

When crop-rotation was the acknowledged system of arable-farming, clover was rightfully considered to be one of the major sources of honey. Indeed, before more stringent descriptions of honey were applied, what was termed "Flower honey" then later "Blossom honey", was often labelled as "Clover honey".

Modern, intensive farming-methods used applied "Nitrates" instead of allowing nitrogen to be fixed into the soil by nodules on the roots of clover plants. Where permanent pastures are laid down, however, clover is an essential ingredient in all but short-term, grass-crop seed mixtures, the quality and vigour of the clover seed having considerable influence on the efficiency of the pasture. There is a distinction between "White clovers" and "Wild, white clovers". The former establish quickly and contribute to the bulk of the hay or silage crop and under good conditions may persist for several years. "Wild, white clovers" are less productive in early life, are dwarf, small-leaved and high tillering but are far more persistent.

The beekeeper may benefit from fields of "Wild, white clover" but not usually until after they have been established for two years. It is only on permenent pasture where such clover is well-cropped by animals, that really heavy nectar-flows occur, although road verges and patches of waste-ground provide a useful supplement.

The lime tree of which there are several varieties, is rightly considered to be one of the major nectar-sources in some parts of Britain. North of the Forth valley in the East however, lime honey in quantity in the hives has not been in evidence dring the past forty years although bees are frequently seen working on the blossom in July. Lime honey is quite distinctive having a light green colour and a pronounced sharp "minty" flavour.

The rose-bay-willow-herb, or fireweed, as it is often called yields a water-white honey which although rather thin and having a tendency to granulate quickly, nevertheless has a fine, delicate flavour. This flower appears to yield nectar best during its first few years of being established.

The dark port-wine-coloured honey from bell heather is secured in fair quantity, particularly on moors which are regularly burned. It is not often appreciated that this source yields earlier in the year than is often thought. In some years this flow starts at the end of June.

The rich, amber-coloured, thixotropic honey from ling heather is much sought after and although a difficult crop both to secure and handle, the financial returns are well worth-while. The ling nectar-flow may start during the third week in July and last only a few days, or in some years the flow does not commence until the second or third week in August and continue until well into September. Best results are obtained on moors above nine hundred feet elevation and where regular, controlled-burning is practised so that the heather plants are under five years old.

There are many other minor nectar-sources all of which are useful and in some seasons combine to give a fair return, but the sources described are those which over the years, yield the bulk of surplus honey. In the East of Scotland, early sources - mainly for their pollen, sycamore, oil-seed-rape, raspberries, bell and ling heather are those which the beekeeper must follow to secure a profitable return. There are indications that farming practices may return to crop rotation with fallow-ground recovery periods, in which case wild-white clovers may yet come into their own again.

Shelter

Areas exist where ample foraging vegetation is available, but which prove poor beekeeping locality, for shelter as well as suitable flora is indispensable. In exposed, windswept localities, flying may be hampered and even when it is possible, nectar secretion is adversely affected.

Humidity pockets exist where, even after hours of hot, drying sunshine, moisture is still retained, and their presence may be indicated by wet undergrowth, grass or soil. These pockets are ideal for nectar secretion and gathering, being sheltered not only from sun on hot, drying days, but from cold winds and air currents during cooler weather. They can range in extent from as little as a few hundred feet to several miles and are generally created by the surrounding terrain, or, to a more limited extent, by vegetatioin, particularly trees in the vicinity.

One of the greatest drawbacks to successful honey production on the Eastern coastal belt of the British Isles is the East wind, with its hard-drying influence. This problem does not arise to the same extent in the West where the humidity is normally higher. Apiaries identical in all other respects, separated perhaps by only a mile or so, can show a great difference in activity. In one, the stocks may be working furiously on a nectar flow while in the other, scarcely a bee is moving. Even the comparatively insensitive human body may feel the slight difference in temperature between two such apiaries. This variation in conditions, although sometimes very slight, can decide the difference between a nectar flow or none.

It is only by trial and error, coupled with observation, that suitable localities can be discovered. Although experienced beekeepers can develop a sort of sixth sense about their choice, an obvious solution is to scatter hives over several likely-looking areas and compare the results.

The importance of good locality cannot be over-stressed. Even in a year of adverse weather and where the poorest type of beekeeping management is practised, there are localities where a reasonable honey crop is always secured. A further important point to consider is that many diseases of bees are endemic to localities.

So much for the first two factors affecting honey production - weather and locality. We now come to the main purpose of this book; to consider the care and management of bee colonies and the techniques employed to ensure that these colonies are ever ready to take advantage of locality and weather.

Chapter III

THE APIARY AND ITS EQUIPMENT

After choosing a likely locality, it is then necessary to select a suitable spot for the setting up of an apiary and to consider how it can be laid out to best advantage.

Accessibility is the first consideration, for unless the apiary is situated in the beekeepers's garden, much unnecessary labour could be involved in the manhandling of hives, supers and other equipment between storage accommodation and apiary.

Shelter from cold prevailing winds plays an important part and can be provided by small trees and shrubs *(Fig 21)*, or even wattle-type fencing, all of which are more efficient than solid wind breaks such as a wall. An over-sheltered site, however, tends to cause damp conditions in the hives over winter *(Fig 20)*. Exposure to maximum sunlight tends to alleviate dampness and does much to ensure better wintering conditions.

A natural water supply situated in a sunny, sheltered spot in the apiary is an advantage, particularly in Spring, otherwise an artificial drinking fountain can be supplied *(Fig 62)*. A stock-proof fence to prevent intrusion by the larger animals completes the layout.

Siting of the hives is determined by their number and the space available.

Drifting

An apiary can have a very neat and business-like appearance when the hives are equally spaced out in a staight line and has the advantage of easy access for the distribution of equipment *(Fig 17)*. There are, however, several disadvantages. As each colony of bees dispenses scent from its fanners at the hive entrance, young bees especially are apt to drift to the colony issuing the greatest scent. This tends to deplete the weaker colonies and upsets the balance of the already strong ones. Drifting is especially noticeable and detrimental in the spring months. Although they have an accurate sense of direction, when the hives are placed close together and are of the same pattern and colour, bees are apt to become confused and drift into the wrong hives. Painting hives different colours, as is done with the entrances of Swiss bee houses, helps to overcome this difficulty since bees are able to distinguish colours apart from red. Nevertheless, screening with foliage is more practical and serves better purposes.

Drifting is undesirable for other reasons. Bees suffering from disease, such as acarine or nosema, may carry the malady to otherwise healthy stocks *(Fig 19)*. Although bees with full honey sacs are usually admitted to a strange colony without trouble, wayward bees can cause fighting at the hive entrance and the resultant uproar can spread to neighbouring hives. Robbing too is more likely to occur when hives are close together.

Perhaps the greatest objection to placing hives closely in open rows is the resultant discomfort to the beekeeper should one stock become unruly. Angry bees from such a stock may harrass the beekeeper throughout the examination of the entire apiary. Setting hives in rows behind each other accentuates the difficulty, as bees from the rear rank tend to drift into the front hives on returning from the field. Bees from the rear rank, flying at head and shoulder level, add to the beekeepers discomfort while he manipulates the front rank.

To prevent drifting, hives should be placed in small groups, well screened from each other by suitable foliage and care taken to ensure that manipulations can be carried out from behind *(Figs 22 & 23)*. Should one stock become upset, it is a simple matter to carry on with manipulations in other groups of hives, then return to it and complete the task if deemed advisable.

Where the flight of bees interferes with animals or passers-by, screening with hedging or wattle fencing can raise the line of flight above head-level and thus out of harm's way.

Hive Stands

Hives should be set up on some support, allowing a current of air to circulate under the floorboards. Four bricks can be used, providing the ground is not overgrown with weeds, two fencing posts make a useful stand for a pair of hives and for migratory beekeeping, perhaps there is nothing to better heavy-guage, corrugated iron cut into suitably-sized pieces *(Fig 24)*. All hives should be tilted forward slightly to allow for drainage of any moisture accumulating inside.

Bee Hives

Individual preference for types of bee hives causes great controversy amongst beekeepers. Here again many sources of beekeeping information simply list the details and measurements of the various hives without comment, so that a beginner is left as bewildered as before and is at the mercy of the arguments of the nearest beekeeper, who may or may not understand all the implications.

A beginner should give careful thought to the type and extent of beekeeping he eventually intends to practise, as this should influence not only the choice of hive, but also the selection of many other items of equipment. If a doubt should arise it would naturally be advisable to choose a type of hive and equipment which, if so desired, could be expanded upon, or, if disposed of, fetch a reasonable second-hand price.

As far as bee colonies and honey production are concerned, no hive is better than another providing it is dry inside and managed properly to ensure ample room. Strong colonies of bees yielding a very good honey crop have been kept in old tea boxes. The hive is simply a tool of the beekeeper and as such must be chosen for the purpose to which it is best suited. Let us examine the merits and demerits of the more popular designs of bee hives.

The W.B.C. hive (Fig 25) reigned supreme for many years and proved very satisfactory. It is rather picturesque with its sloping contours and a few attractively-painted, look well in a carefully kept garden. The outer casings or "lifts" give an added protection of insulation, which is an advantage for comb honey production. Set against these good points there are many disadvantages. The W.B.C. hive is costly to buy, complicated to make and generally has a very poor second-hand value. Because of its shape it is difficult both to secure and transport and is, therefore, unsuitable for migratory beekeeping. More storage space is required for the various hive parts when they are not in use and in manipulation, much time and energy is expended in removing and replacing the outer lifts. Some methods of dealing with swarming colonies are rendered so complicated with this type of hive as to make them impracticable. Apart from appearance, there is little to recommend the W.B.C. hive for modern beekeeping. True, it is possible to buy second-hand hives of this design quite cheaply, but a would-be purchaser should check each hive part. Owing to variations in manufacture, all W.B.C. hive parts are not interchangeable.

The Glen hive (Fig 26) with its fifteen frames has proved extremely satisfactory in favoured localities, the large brood chamber with proper management, giving adequate room for raising powerful colonies. It has, however, all the disadvantages of the W.B.C. with the added objection of the chambers being heavy and unwieldy when full.

Fig. 17. Hives set close together in rows encourage drifting and are difficult to manage.

Fig. 18. Non-standardisation causes much unnecessary work.

Fig. 19. Number of hives from unknown sources could be means of contacting disease *(Photo MAFF)*

Fig. 20. Hives under trees give bad wintering conditions.

Fig. 21. Screening with shrubbery.

Fig. 22. Access behind hives makes handling easier.

Fig. 23. A pair of hives on stand makes ideal working conditions.

Fig. 24. Hive on corrugated iron stand.

American Hives (Fig 27). The Langstroth and Dadant hives cannot be lightly dismissed as they are ideal for various methods of beekeeping and are used by some of the biggest beekeeping concerns in the country. They are relatively cheap and easy to make, suitable for migratory beekeeping, easily stored and ideal for using in all methods of treating swarming colonies. What then are their disadvantages?

Specialised equipment is required to deal with the larger frames *(Fig 34)* when extracting and in many parts of the country the second-hand value is somewhat restricted. The purchasing or selling of nuclei on these large frames which do not fit into British equipment is limited. The chambers when full are rather heavy to handle when a beekeeper is working single-handed. Perhaps the greatest disadvantage is that those American hives are not so versatile as those with British Standard frames when restriction of interior space is desired. In average years it is sometimes expedient to limit the brood chamber area in the hope of securing surplus honey in the honey supers. This applies especially in heather honey production. Although it is possible to restrict such space in larger hives by the use of division boards, this necessitates further labour and, on occasion, the transporting of larger bulk than is necessary.

One great advantage of the deep frames is the extensive, unbroken brood-rearing area available to the colony. However, as will be shown, there is a considerable saving of labour when such a brood area can be broken in the middle for inspection.

The National Hive (Fig 28) became popular over the years. It is comparatively cheap to buy though not so easy to make, suitable for migratory beekeeping, easily stored, versatile in contraction or expansion, holds its second-hand value fairly well, its chambers are of reasonable weight when full and it is adaptable to all methods of beekeeping.

Some beekeepers have used the *British Commercial hive* with its 16 x 10 inch frames with success. Its outside dimensions are the same as the National so that supers and standard chambers are interchangeable. The British Commercial hive has both the advantages and disadvantages of the American hives.

The Wormit Commercial hive (Fig 29) is similar to the National but is slightly more costly and more difficult to make, having a raised fillet round the edges of supers and chambers *(Fig 31).* This makes an extremely secure and easily transportable hive, but can lead to difficulty when separating chambers, as the hive tool cannot be easily inserted between joints to act as a lever and prise down sticking frames.

The Smith hive (Fig 30) has all the advantages of the National as well as being cheaper to buy and easier to make. Like the American hives its bee space is over the tops of the frames instead of under them, as with all other British hives *(Fig 32).* This makes manipulation just a trifle smoother. The hand holds cut in the front and back of the chambers as well as the sides are of considerable advantage, although the recessed sides of the improved National act similarly.

An objection put forward by some beekeepers to the Smith hive is that, like American hives, the frames have short lugs and are thought more difficult to manipulate than the full-sized British Standard frame *(Fig 34).*

These then are the hives! Which to choose? The Glen and Wormit hive are now somewhat of a rarity and are no longer being manufactured. It is interesting to note that in Northern Europe including Scandinavia, the size of combs in general use, corresponds roughly to the dimensions of the British Standard frame. Unless one intends to build up to a commercial enterprise of more than five hundred stocks in Britain, in which case the Langstroth may be considered, the choice depends on what part of the country the operation is to be set-up. Because of the possible value of hives when sold second-hand, Nationals are recommended South of the Border and Smiths for beekeepers in Scotland.

Although double-walled hives can be painted it is not advisable to paint single-walled hives, as will be discussed in wintering bees. Single-walled hives are best treated with creosote, or better still, with a wood preservative such as Cuprinol. The latter is initially more expensive, but lasts longer and renders the hive parts cleaner to handle. Care should be taken to select a wood preservative which does not contain any form of insecticide. Both sides of the floor boards and only the outside and edges of the chambers should be treated in this way and if creosote is preferred, care should be taken that any excess does not saturate the inside of the chambers as this can lead to the tainting of honey. Both creosote and wood preservative can be applied by brush to occupied hives during cold weather, but if a large amount of equipment is to be treated, a shallow tray filled with the medium into which the parts can be dipped will expedite matters considerably.

Alighting boards on hives are not a necessity. True, they tend to keep down plant growth from the hive entrance, but when hives have to be moved they can be a hindrance. If the beekeeper feels alighting boards to be an advantage it is an easy matter to lay a flat piece of wood or asbestos sheeting in front of the hive entrance *(Fig 37).* Floor boards should be kept as simple as possible. For National and Smith hives a floorboard with ¾ in. entrance on one side and ⅜ in. on the reverse without any slope is quite satisfactory.

Some prefer to make their own hives and provided care is taken and proper material used, these are often quite serviceable. For single-walled hives only a porous wood such as Red Cedar should be used if dry conditions in the hives are to be maintained over winter. The commonest faults with home-made hives are warping due to the use of improperly seasoned or unsuitable timber and shrinking, for which allowance should be made.

For smooth manipulation, hive parts must be accurate. There are few factors calculated to exasperate both bees and beekeeper so much as ill-fitting hives which have brace comb and propolis sticking to every movable part.

Various materials are used for hive roofs, most of which give a perfectly watertight covering. For migratory beekeeping, a material which will stand up to a fair measure of wear and tear is desirable and metal roofs are best suited. Aluminium is rather soft and inclined to tear should it be caught on a sharp projection, but galvanised iron, although slightly heavier to handle, is superior.

In damp localities the ventilation holes on many hives are inadequate and if wet conditions are observed inside the hives, these holes should be enlarged.

Up to the present, all standard makes of hives in Europe and USA have telescopic roofs - that is roofs which are slightly larger than the other hive parts and which fit over the hive-proper, like the lid of a shoe-box. The writer copied the Australian-Langstroth hive-roof with sizes adapted to fit the Smith hive. These roofs are of the same length and breadth as the hive-chambers and have an inner cavity of 2 inches between the bottom rims and the upper casing of the flat roof-top.

The Australian roof when fitted to a hive, rests on it just like a very shallow-super, so it is necessary to use some form of hive-locking device to keep it in place. This roof acts as a combined roof, cover-board and screen-board for travelling, two pairs of 1 inch holes covered with perforated-zinc at front and back allow ventilation. Some of these roofs were used experimentally for over-wintering bee-colonies and were found to be entirely satisfactory.

Although the bulk of manufactured hives are still made from selected timbers, there is an increasing volume of hives being made from plastics. The early models fashioned in fibre-glass were not successful because of excessive condensation during winter. The early expanded-polystyrene hives were not robust enough to withstand normal wear-and-tear in the apiary and bees were apt to chew holes in the rather soft material. Newly-developed treatments, however, have strengthened this

Fig. 25. Double-walled W.B.C. hive

Fig. 26. The Glen hive is of large dimensions

Fig. 27. Langstroth hive with roof and super removed

Fig. 28. Improved National and National hives

Fig. 29. Wormit Commercial hive showing Williamson floor board

Fig. 30. Smith hive with flush floor board

Fig. 31. Corner of Wormit hive showing raised fillet

Fig. 32. Corner of Smith hive showing top bee space

13

material considerably and the toughened outer-surfaces no longer permit bees to chew through them. As was found in Scandinavia and other cold-country climates, the conservation of heat during winter by the use of polystyrene was of considerable benefit but there was a problem of increased condensation with the hives. To compensate for this, a special deep, double-floorboard was developed, the base of which is solid like an ordinary hive floor but which has a top platform covered with metal gauze a few inches above it. This allows bees to fly from the space between the brood-chamber and the top platform, excludes predators like mice, but at the same time gives a large bottom area for ventilation.

Other Hive Accessories.

Although cover cloths are widely used and have the advantage of being able to be peeled back to expose small areas of frames at a time, cover or crown boards are cleaner to use, more durable and can be utilised for various manipulations. A cut-away swivel portion of the crown board rim to provide an entrance is necessary for at least one method of treating a swarming stock (Fig 127).

There are two designs of queen excluder, the Waldron and the zinc slotted. Although the Waldron is stronger and more rigid than the zinc, it is doubtful if the much higher price is justified. Zinc excluders, with or without framing, operate quite satisfactorily. When new, zinc excluders present a sharp edge where the machine-cut slots are made and to prevent undue wearing of bees' wings and bodies, should be gently rubbed over with a piece of emery cloth.

Queen excluders made from plastic, have been in operation for some years and no complaints have been received about their suitability.

The final hive part required is a screen board. This is a framework of wood approximately ⅜ inch thick to which is affixed a piece of wire cloth or perforated zinc (⅛ inch hole gauge), the latter preferably as it is more robust and easier to clean. Although the screen board is primarily used when transporting stocks, it has many other uses.

With most methods of honey production a beekeeper should endeavour to build up each hive to consist of one floorboard, two brood chambers, one queen excluder, three shallow supers or section crates, one crown baord, one screen board and one roof, together with a few spare brood chambers for each apiary.

Frames and Spacing.

There are several types of frames and methods of spacing them to choose from. The British Standard frame with metal end spacing is still in common use and is perfectly satisfactory (Fig 33). When stocks are being transported, however, and if the frames in supers or brood chambers are new, there is a risk of the frames swinging and becoming displaced. When extracting, metal ends are best removed from the honey frames and a little time is wasted doing so and subsequently replacing them.

Hoffman self-spacing frames (Fig 35) are becoming increasingly popular for use in the brood chambers for although more expensive and more difficult to make, form a compact mass ideally suited for transit. One small objection to their use is the slight propolising by the bees between frames. This, however, is easily broken apart by a twist of the hive tool. The wisdom of the British Standard Specifiction of 1⅜ inch spacing for this type of frame has been questioned, as, when eleven frames are inserted in a National or Smith brood chamber, a space is left which must be filled with a dummy board to prevent the building of a brace comb. When twelve frames are inserted, any slight swelling of the wood, or the subsequent propolising between frames, makes the removal of combs a very difficult proposition. As dummy boards serve little useful purpose, many consider the 1⅜ inch spacing to be far from satisfactory.

1 $\frac{13}{32}$ inch (Generally referred to as 1½ inch) spacing Hoffman frames with 2½ inch shoulders, of whch eleven fit into the brood chambers leaving a small space for manoeuvring can be obtained and are more satisfactory. Because of the short-lug frames used in the Smith hive, metal ended standard frames are not ideal, but can be used in conjunction with Hoffman frames by bending down the bottom wing of the metal end until such time as they can be discarded.

British Standard shallow frames are very suitable for use in the honey supers, being drawn out on narrow metal ends before extracting and being subsequently fitted with wide metal ends.

The Manley type self-spacing shallow frame (Fig 36) is proving a great asset in many ways. Once the comb is properly drawn out, much labour is saved during uncapping, the wooden frame acting as a guide for the uncapping knife. This frame is invaluable for cut comb or wrapped honey production.

For section honey production, the older design of the National and Smith section crates (Fig 39), which held 32 sections, proved too large in normal years, the outside rows of sections often being left unfinished. The newer Smith section crate (Fig 40) with its insulating spaces in which bees can cluster, is a vast improvement.

In both the National and the Smith hive, old W..C. section crates, which hold 21 sections, can be used (Fig 38). These crates can often be bought very cheaply second-hand and are easily made or adapted. All that is generally required is to plane or chisel the flanges on either side of the crate, which then fits into a National or Smith empty super. The advantage of the W.B.C. hive's insulation for section production is now duplicated in a single-walled hive.

Castle spacing, so-called because of the resemblance to the top of a caslte turret, often tempts beekeepers to try them out, as, with them, no spacing is required on the frames. Instead, the frames rest on these spacers, which are affixed to the hive body. On first reflection this may appear to be a great improvement, but it will be found in practice that they are practically worthless. With normal frame spacing, frames are able to be prised apart by the hive tool, as there is always a certain amount of brace comb present. With castle spacing, however, this prising is impossible and should brace comb be present it is necessary to cut it with a knife before removing the frame.

Fig. 33. British Standard frame fitted with wired foundation and metal end spacers.

Fig. 34. Comparison of frame sizes. Modified Dadant, Langstroth, British Standard and British Standard with cut-down lugs for Smith Hive.

Fig. 35. Smith brood chamber with 1½" Hoffman self-spacing frames.

Fig. 36. Smith super with Manley-type closed-end frames.

Fig. 37. An odd piece of wood serves as a suitable alighting board.

Fig. 38. Cut-down W.B.C. section crate fits inside a Smith or National super.

Fig. 39 Old pattern Smith and National section crates were too large for section production, but can be utilised for plastic "Cobana" section holders.

Fig. 40 New pattern Smith section crate.

Chapter IV

MOVING BEES.

Until recent years, beekeepers in these parts looked forward to the annual move to the heather with mixed feelings. Many an amusing tale was told of dancing figures fleeing madly into the undergrowth pursued by hordes of angry bees, following the untimely release of a colony as it clattered from a lorry onto the hard roadway. Those were the days when such a trip was leisurely contemplated and still more leisurely performed, seldom without some mishap which added spice and variety to the proceedings. With the volume of traffic now on the roads and migratory beekeeping often involving several moves a year, few beekeepers can afford such pleasantries, so that moving bees has been reduced to a fine art.

Securing double-walled hives is not an easy task, as the inside chambers should be firmly secured to the floor board. This can be accomplished by the use of iron brackets or 1¼ in. wooden batons. Care must be taken to ensure the firm closure of the inside entrance.

Single-walled hives are comparatively easy to prepare and many methods can be employed. ¼ in. thick wooden slats, 2 in.-3 in. wide, secured with wire nails to floorboard and chambers on each side, provide a rigid structure which stands up well to travelling, but the drawback to this method is the time involved and the subsequent removal and replacement of these fixings should any examination of the stock be necessary.

The steel banding machine *(Fig 45)* makes a very satisfactory job of securing hives, but it is not within the scope of the smaller beekeeper to own one of these rather expensive machines. With regard to examinations, the band has the same disadvantage as wooden slats. With this method it is advisable to insert small pieces of angle aluminium in the floor board and screen board to prevent the band from biting into the soft wood.

Australian lock slides (Fig 45) are a good investment for the average beekeeper, for although the initial cost has to be borne, the fittings being permanent and reliable for transit, keep the hives secure throughout the year. There are many advantages to this type of fitting, not the least of which is their ease of being fastened or opened. As they are fitted separately to each hive joint, it is a simple matter to open the hive at any one place without disturbing the other junctions.

The lock slide rails must be carefully positioned with a template and firmly screwed to the wood, care being taken to ensure that the template is used from alternate corners of the hive. This allows any hive part to fit anywhere in the hive no matter whether it be put on front or back first. Before moving, the lock slides should be tapped firmly in place with a small cross pein hammer *(Fig 46)* or in an emergency, with a hive tool. When framed queen excluders are used, extra-wide slides are available to compensate for the extra width of joint between parts. The compactness of the lock slides allows the hive parts to be set inside an upturned roof.

There is always the risk of suffocation of colonies awaiting or during transit, but proper precautions can usually prevent this. Some beekeepers have moved stocks successfully over the years without even the use of screen boards, but one has only to witness once a lorry-load of bee colonies which have been suffocated to realise the tremendous damage that can arise through indifferent preparations. The practice of closing the hive entrance with a strip of perforated zinc or wire gauze is not a good one. Bees when confined are apt to rush to any source of ventilation or light and this could have drastic results in the brood chamber. A struggling crowd of bees can very quickly block the little ventilation supplied at a hive entrance and within a short time, the temperature inside the hive may rise to such an extent that the wax combs melt and there is nothing left of the stock save a heap of dead brood and

bees covered in sticky honey and ruined combs. Even although such damage is not immediately apparent, over-heating is detrimental to the brood and after unventilated confinement, the removal of dead larvae from an affected hive can be observed days after the move has taken place.

A screen board on the upper chamber tends to draw bees there, away from the brood chamber out of harm's way. Where hives are stacked in tiers it is necessary to adopt some method of spacing over the screen boards to ensure circulation of fresh air. Stocks with newly-gathered nectar or "green" honey should never be moved.

Screen boards are best fastened to the uppermost chamber with four wire nails driven through the framework of the screen into the thickest wall of the hive chamber *(Fig 43)*. In National and Smith hives these are the side walls and the same nail-holes in the screenboard can be used time and again, the board being carefully prised off with a hive tool after each move.

Even if all these precautions are taken, however, there is no guarantee that all will be well. For example, a long confinement on a hot day can do immeasurable damage and other unexpected factors can test the resourcefulness of the beekeeper.

A solid wooden block of a size to give a finger-tight fit can be used to close the hive entrances *(Fig. 44)*. Nails or staples previously driven into the sides of the hive floor board prevent the blocks from being pushed too far into the interior, and should be set so that when the block is in position it is flush with the entrance *(Fig. 42)*. Should the block seem over-slack or too short, two small pieces of perforated zinc can be affixed to both block and floor board with drawing pins. A small screwdriver is most useful to assist withdrawal *(Fig.48)*.

Pieces of plumber's lagging felt cut to suitable lengths and pushed in double with a hive tool provide a satisfactory closure for odd hives. Strips of foam plastic cut to the desired sizes is a recent innovation.

A recommended Procedure.

The following procedure has proved very satisfactory. During daylight, the cover boards are removed and the screen boards fixed in position. At the same time entrance blocks are checked with the entrances and laid on top of the hives.

When bees have stopped flying in the evening, or earlier if it is a wet or cold day, the entrance block is gently inserted, using a puff of smoke if the bees are inquisitive or clustering at the entrance. The lock slides are tapped home with a cross pien hammer, then the roof removed and placed upside down beside the hive. The crown board is placed, sticky side up, in the inverted roof. This prevents it from adhering to the roof, with the subsequent risk of damage when attempting to dislodge it. The hive is now manoeuvred first cornerwise on the roof, then lowered gently into it. If the roofs are numbered, or have some other distinguishing marks, the hives should be positioned so that the entrances face the marks. This simplifies matters when positioning in the new site, especially if it is dark.

It will be agreed that the weakest joint in the hive and that which generally gives trouble in transit, is between floorboards and bottom brood chamber. By inserting the hive into the up-turned roof, this joint is well protected and the entrance block held securely in place *(Fig. 47)*.

Depending on the weight of hives and on labour available, a form of carrier may be employed. Metal hive carriers with hooks cannot be used with this latter method, but a wooden stretcher has been found most satisfactory.

Fig. 41. Securing hive with steel tape banding machine.

Fig. 42. Flush floor board showing position of stop nails and entrance block partly open.

Fig. 43. Fixing screen board with four wire nails. Colony is subdued first of all.

Fig. 44. Inserting entrance block. Smoker is used to drive in inquisitive bees.

Fig. 45. Lock slides, rails and wedge.

Fig. 46. Wedge tapped home with cross pien hammer.

Fig. 47. Hive set in inverted roof ready for transit.

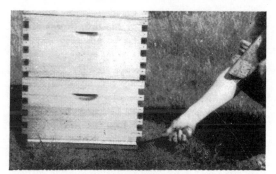

Fig. 48. Screwdriver used for removal of entrance block at destination.

The metal roof of the hive allows the unit to be slid along the floor of the transport with a minimum of effort, which is an advantage in confined space or when hives are heavy. Stocks travel better if the frames in the hive run parallel to the direction of travel. This helps to prevent swinging of the frames and allows more ventilation.

The use of the Australian flush-fitting roof saves the work of preparing stocks prior to moving, as this roof acts as a screen-board and is already in position. All that is necessary, is to secure the entrances and check that the hive fixtures are tight. The writer used lock-slides to fix these roofs to the hives and they were perfectly satisfactory. These lock-slides however are now obsolete in Australia having been superseded by triangular, spring-wire clips whch are permanently fitted to the tops of chambers by coach-screws. When in the closed position, the clips are sprung into place round and between three further screws set near the bottom of the added chamber or roof.

On arrival, all hives should be unloaded and set in position before being opened. If a few are opened immediately the bees from them may harass the beekeeper as he attends to the others. During darkness it is a good plan to check the number of entrance blocks removed against the number of hives moved, as it has been known for an odd hive or two to be left behind securely closed. The screen board can be removed and replaced with the cover board after a few hours, or at a later examination.

Smoker, veil, carbolic cloth, odd pieces of wood, nails, hammer and a daub of plasticine are useful accessories on such a mission should any unforeseen or unfortunate accident occur.

Stocks of bees moved during summer sometimes show a tendency to rear queen cells shortly afterwards, with the possible danger of loss of swarms. The removal of these cells about a week after the move, however, generally allows the colony to settle without further trouble.

It has been said that the foundation for the year's honey crop is laid the previous year and this statement is widely accepted by experienced beekeepers. For a colony to emerge strong and healthy in the spring, it requires to go into winter with dry conditions inside the hive, freedom from disease and an adequate supply of suitable stores positioned properly in relation to the winter cluster. In addition, a large force of bees, which will act as nurses when brood rearing commences, is necessary.

The examination of a natural colony of bees *(Fig. 49)*, reveals a set pattern in the relative positions of brood, pollen and honey stores. During the height of the summer season such a colony has the lower parts of its combs reserved for brood rearing and although honey is sometimes stored on the flanks of the brood nest, a goodly amount is always stored above. As the season progresses, brood rearing dwindles and although some of the vacated cells may be used for the storing of later honey crops, brood is generally present until the last of the nectar flows have ceased. Thus the beginning of winter finds a colony with an area of empty cells on which to form a cluster and a canopy of honey above.

Starving in the midst of Plenty

With modern beekeeping methods the surplus honey removed in supers is comparable with this canopy and if proper wintering conditions are to be observed, stores must be returned to their natural position in the hive. During the winter months the colony eats upwards into its stores and may arrive at a position near the tops of the combs where no honey is available above. If a long, unbroken spell of frosty weather ensues, or if the colony is weak, the cluster may be unable to expand or cross over to fresh areas of stores and consequently may die of starvation *(Figs. 50 and 51)*.

The gripping story of Scott's expedition to the Antartic illustrates this condition. Because of severe weather conditions and hostile terrain, Scott and his companions were unable to travel back to base camp where ample supplies of food and fuel were available, and so perished. So too can a cluster of bees die in the winter, although the "hostile terrain" in this instance may be only a few inches of empty comb or wood. If, however, food is available immediately above, the cluster is able to eat upwards following its self-created warmth.

Winter Sunshine

The heat of winter sunshine, though it be for a brief hour or so, may penetrate a hive and raise the temperature within to such an extent that the cluster can change its position to fresh areas of food. The siting of hives so that they receive the maximum exposure of sunlight during winter adds greatly to good wintering, not only helping to prevent isolation starvation, but also allowing bees to emerge for all-important cleansing flights and tending to disperse dampness in the hive itself. Hives situated in a damp pocket seldom winter satisfactorily and although shelter is advantageous, it should not be sought to the exclusion of sunlight and airiness.

Sometimes after a fall of snow a bright sunny day follows and reflected light may entice bees out if the temperature is high enough. Bees landing on the snow-covered ground can get chilled and a certain death rate may result *(Fig. 56)*. In conditions like this, it is a simple matter to place shade boards over the entrance until the danger has passed.

Let's Get Together

When a hive has been stripped of all its supers so that only a single brood chamber remains, a common practice is to feed heavily with sugar syrup, or to insert solid combs of honey in place of empty or partially filled ones to attain sufficient weight of stores for wintering. The resultant conditions are not always ideal.

If a dumpling is placed on a plate it will remain hot for a considerable time, but if cut into thin slices a larger surface is exposed to the atmosphere and it cools rapidly. Similarly, if a cluster of bees is broken into thin seams by thick, insulating layers of honey, more difficulty will be experienced in maintaining the necessary temperature. Indeed, many colonies although surviving the winter, lose a proportion of their numbers through this condition, the seams of dead bees being readily observed on the outside combs. A natural colony demonstrates that proper clustering space is necessary.

If it is preferred to winter colonies on single brood chambers, it is advantageous to give extra clustering space, as the amount of food required should occupy most of the chamber. Admittedly a colony will make clustering space for itself after consuming some of the stores, but if frosty weather prevails during the early part of the winter, this does not apply. Suitable space can be given by inserting a shallow or deep super of old drawn comb between floor board and brood chamber, or if these combs are not available, an empty super will serve the purpose. If the latter method is used and the brood chamber is indeed packed with honey, the cluster can sometimes be seen hanging like a swarm from the bottom combs of the brood chamber.

A double brood chamber system offers superior wintering conditions, as generally by autumn the top brood chamber contains adequate stores, while the bottom one not only has stores, but also valuable clustering space after the last of the brood has hatched out. How the wintering cluster travels upwards can readily be demonstrated in such a hive, for spring examination will normally reveal that the colony then occupies an area near the top which is usually flanked by stores *(Fig. 50)*. These observations apply to British standard frame chambers and these results are not so evident in American type hives which have greater comb areas.

Over the Top

A colony cluster on reaching the top extremities of its hive and having utilised the food in its path, may be able with the help of sunlight to cross over the tops of the combs to new stores. A solid obstacle such as a quilt placed hard down over the top combs prevents this movement and consequently this lack of bee space contributes to more deaths by starvation. A bee space or winter passage is ready-made when using a properly constructed crown board, but if quilts are preferred, short pieces of twig or garden cane laid at right angles across the frame tops will provide satisfactory spacing.

Mak' Sikkar (Make Sure)

Periodical examinations of colonies during the winter are advisable to ensure that food is always present on top of the cluster position. When it is noticed that the colony lacks food above the cluster, the situation should be remedied at once. A super of honey placed on top of the brood chamber is a satisfactory method, but failing that, the administering of a cake of candy, syrup in a suitable feeder, or even a comb of honey laid on its face across the frame tops, will alleviate immediate starvation until such time as more satisfactory methods can be employed.

Ventilation

Many colonies, while surviving the rigours of winter, emerge in the spring weakened through lack of proper ventilation in their hives. Hives prepared for wintering often have their en-

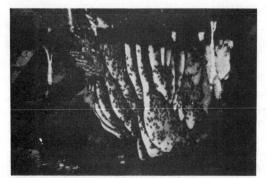

Fig. 49. *Formation of natural colony.*

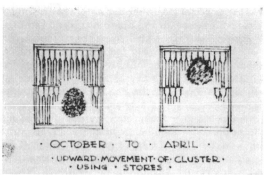

Fig. 50. *Diagram of movement of winter cluster.*

Fig. 51 *Comb from stock dead of isolation starvation.*

Fig. 52. *Comb from stock dead of absolute starvation.*

Fig. 53. *Water blister on painted hive. Photo Northumberland County Council.*

Fig. 54. *Entrance block from hive showing propolis barrier built by Caucasian bees.*

Fig. 55. *Removal of crown board and adding empty super helps to alleviate dampness in hive.*

Fig. 56 *Bees chilled on snow after being enticed out by reflected light.*

20

trances reduced to a few inches and it was common practice to add masses of packing in the form of old sacks, newspapers, waterproofs and, in fact, any type of cast-off clothing that the beekeeper could lay his hand on. It was certainly meritorious of the beekeeper to go to all this trouble to keep his bees "warm", but the examination of such prepared hives during winter often shows that far from satisfactory results are achieved, the "warm" packing so carefully supplied often being damp, or even soaking wet.

Although every care should be taken to ensure that hive roofs are watertight, dampness does not necessarily come directly from outside, but can be caused partly by moisture vapour being drawn in at the entrance by the heat of the cluster and partly given off by the cluster itself, condensing on the upper extremities of the hive. In any modern building ventilation is afforded in the rooms by windows, fireplaces and, as in the case of school-rooms or halls, a ventilator may be installed in the ceiling. This position is advantageous for such rooms are built to accommodate large numbers of people and the warm air containing water vapour rises and can rapidly escape.

Modern hives have ventilator holes in their roofs, those of double-walled varieties consisting of the cone escape at one end and a hole covered with perforated zinc at the other, while single-walled hives have two perforated zinc-covered holes at opposite sides. On the roofs of the latter are incorporated fillets of wood which leave a space of an inch or so between brood chamber and roof top when the roof is in position. These ventilation holes allow a through draught of air which carries away fouled and moisture-laden atmosphere, but if impervious packing is used, ventilation is blocked. Resultant condensation on this material can be readily observed in the extreme case where glass cover boards are used. If it is thought desirable to use packing, though its value is doubtful in this country, porous material should be used.

Crown boards are preferable to packing, but to ensure through ventilation the feed hole should be left open. An argument is put forward by some who have found that by covering the feed hole with perforated zinc, bees will fill up the mesh with propolis, the inference being that bees dislike this through draught and take steps to close it. While it is true that they may block up this perforated zinc, it is also true that they may block up any space in the hive with which they have contact if it is less than a bee space. If the feed hole is left open, bees will not normally attempt to block up this orifice and similarly, if a top entrance is provided, they will respect it and leave it open. Even with a hole left open in a crown board, ideal ventilation is not necessarily provided and dampness is often seen on the crown board itself, particularly at the outer corners. Lifting the board on match sticks or pieces of broken section wood allows more ventilation and helps to prevent this.

Closing the entrance to a few inches impedes ventilation, moisture pockets often forming at the front corners of the floor board and the accumulation of wax debris piling up in these positions affords harbour for fungoid growths *(Fig. 197)*.

The fact that Caucasian bees build a barrier of propolis at the hive entrance is quoted as another argument that bees dislike through ventilation. Examination of these barriers, however, shows that they consist mainly of pillars or columns of propolis supporting an arch which leaves a space slightly less than ⅜ inch. This often forms a barrier to mice but does not impede through ventilation *(Fig. 54)*.

Pick 'em up

Double-walled hives are generally constructed with legs and the problem of under-ventilation does not arise, but single-walled hives should not be placed flat on the ground or directly on a concrete or slate slab. Moisture would be drawn into the wood by capillary action and once again, would cause dampness inside. These hives should be placed on stands so that a 6 inch. space at least is left and care should be taken to prevent foliage growing round to interfere with the ventilation.

No Paint

Double-walled hives have an air space between inner chambers and outer lifts, so that painting the exterior is not injurious, as air can circulate in the space provided. With single-walled hives, however, paint, particularly good-quality, gloss paint, can lead once again to dampness, which, coming from the inside of the hive, percolates through the wood and condenses on the inside surface of the paint. In extreme cases, large blisters appear *(Fig. 53)*. When broken, they show that a thin film of water is encased between the wood of the hive and the paintwork; thus the hive proper is encased in dampness. Single-walled, red cedar hives are best treated with wood preservative, which protects the wood from rotting, keeps the hives waterproof to a certain extent and, what is more important, allows the wood to breathe.

Effects of dampness

Complaints are heard about combs containing mouldy pollen, a condition brought about by a combination of circumstances, bad placing of stores being the chief cause. Pollen-clogged combs generally flank the extremity of a brood nest, such stores being placed in cells which are covered by a thin layer of honey before being capped over.

If honey stores are not available on top of the winter cluster, these pollen cells may be uncapped, the honey utilised and the pollen quickly becomes mouldy on being exposed to damp conditions.

Sodden packing on hive parts lowers the temperature of a hive due to latent heat being drawn from the immediate surroundings as the moisture evaporates, even although outside conditions may be favourable.

Honey is hygroscopic, i.e. it has a chemical attraction to water, thus any exposed honey in a damp hive is liable to become diluted in the moisture it has itself absorbed. This diluted honey can then be readily attacked by ever-present yeast spores and fermentation follows. Fermented stores when used by bees may cause dysentery and aggravate adult diseases.

Remedies

Where damp apiary conditions are forced upon the beekeeper, or if dampness is suspected in a hive during winter, the following course is suggested. An empty super is placed directly on top of the brood chamber or chambers, neither packing nor crown board being used, so that the roof rests on the empty super provided *(Fig.55)*. Thus it can be removed at any time with little disturbance to the colony, enabling the beekeeper to examine the hive interior and check up on the position of the winter cluster. In extreme cases, it is an advantage to remove the two outside combs from the brood chambers to allow a current of air to circulate round the remaining combs.

Although colonies winter exceptionally well under such conditions it may be felt that when brood rearing commences in February, conservation of heat is desirable and many beekeepers add packing at this time. In practice, however, colonies of roughly the same strength set side by side, some with packing and others without, have no noticeable difference in their build-up. It must be remembered that the empty super has to be filled with combs before the first nectar flow commences, otherwise a heartbreaking conglomeration of brace comb may fill the cavity.

Should such a mishap occur, the situation can be remedied by using the following procedure, providing the weather is warm enough for bees to fly. A hive tool is used to prise up the super containing the brace comb, just enough so that a cheese-wire or similar, with handles at each end, can be slipped in through the joint with a sawing motion which effectively severs the comb between the hive parts.

The freed super with contents is now lifted temporarily onto an upturned roof then the hive is re-assembled thus; the super with its brace comb is placed directly on the floor board and covered with a queen excluder. The brood chamber or chambers, are placed on top of the excluder then another queen excluder added, over which an extra super with preferably drawn combs is placed. The brood chambers are now sandwiched by queen excluders with the super of brace comb at the bottom and a super of empty combs above. It is advisable to restrict the hive entrance to avoid thr risk of robbing.

Bees dislike having their honey stored in this unnatural position so within a week or two, they will have removed the honey from the brace comb and stored it above in the new super.

It is then an easy matter to remove the offending super with its empty brace comb, shake off the bees and restore the hive to its normal arrangement.

This manipulation can also be used to advantage to clear brood and stores from old or damaged combs taken from hives or feral colonies. It can also be employed to remove stores and brood from a straw skep, in which case the skep is placed on the floorboard with its mouth upward, the whole being encased inside empty brood chambers or supers.

The feeding of bees can be divided into three categories. They are Spring, or Stimulative Feeding, Emergency Feeding and Autumn Feeding.

Spring Feeding

Spring, or stimulative feeding means the feeding of colonies on a thin syrup in small quantities. This is carried out in the belief that so treated, they would be influenced in the same way as if early nectar sources were available and accessible and so build up to strength to take full advantage of early honey sources in the locality. Certainly the maxim "breed bees for the honey flow - not on it", is a very sound one, but experiments and observations indicate that this type of feeding makes little difference, if any, to colony build-up, providing adequate stores are already present in the hive and there is an accessible water supply.

During cold spring seasons, bees are sometimes observed discarding granulated honey, which can be seen scattered about the entrance of the hive *(Fig. 72)*. Ling heather and raspberry honey in particular are more subject to this treatment. A few spoonfuls of sugar dissolved in water, supplied in a suitable feeder, is quickly taken down and such wastage of food generally ceases immediately.

Water is an important contribution to colony build-up in spring as it is required for the dilution of stores carried through the winter for suitable brood feeding. Spring feeding appears to be of no advantage where an apiary is in a protected position and which has a suitable water supply within the same shelter *(Fig. 62)*. Foraging bees have thus an easy sheltered passage between hive and water supply and providing adequate food supplies are in the hive, a maximum build-up is assured. Where the beekeeper is forced to site his stocks in an exposed situation the feeding of thin syrup or sweetened water gives colonies the required moisture with consequent quicker build-up.

Emergency Feeding

Although bees are sometimes fed in the spring months it does not necessarily follow that it is done with the stimulative question in mind. A food shortage may arise through lack of sufficient stores being left the previous autumn, or when winter weather has caused an excessive consumption of stores; thus a beekeeper may find his stocks on the verge of starvation the following spring. In such cases food must be supplied and, equally important, supplied in a postion where bees have easy access to it. Although carried out in spring, such feeding is better termed emergency feeding.

The most drastic form of emergency feeding has to be applied when a stock is so depleted in food that the bees are falling off the combs and may lie in a heap on the floor of the hive. This condition may arise even in summer, particularly during the month of June when colonies have used up all earlier sources and outside nectar sources are not available. Dead larvae being removed from the hive is an external sign of such starvation and although to have a colony in such a state is very bad beekeeping, if caught in time a remedy can be applied. Any brood present, however, may already have suffered much damage.

A few tablespoonfuls of sugar should be dissolved in warm water in a honey jar, the lid of which has been perforated with a dozen holes made by a frame nail, then the solution sprinkled onto the starving bees *(Fig. 57)*. If not too late the bees will pass round this food and within a short time return to the combs, when a more substantial form of feeding can be given.

The method of administering feeding to a colony during cold weather in winter and early spring, when the temperature at night is often low, must be carefully considered. In such conditions the winter cluster may be rendered immobile and many types of feeder prove useless as bees are unable to leave the cluster and travel over a cold area to reach the food. In many cases some types of feeder have been found on colonies dead from starvation although filled with perfectly good sugar syrup.

This condition is a form of isolation starvation.

Food in cold weather must be placed in close proximity to the cluster. A most suitable type of feeder for this purpose can be made from a syrup or honey tin with a friction closing lid, which has from twelve to twenty holes pierced in it with a frame nail *(Fig. 59)*. A seven or fourteen pound, squat, lacquered honey tin is ideal for the purpose as it holds a fair quantity of syrup, is slow to corrode, is of a size which can be conveniently set inside an empty shallow super without danger of the roof rocking on it *(Fig. 61)* and, because of its handle, a number can be carried at one time *(Fig. 60)*.

The tin is almost filled with syrup, the lid forced tightly in place and the feeder is now ready to be placed in the stock, perforated lid side down, as near to the cluster as possible. It is often an advantage to remove the crown board completely to locate the position of the cluster so that the feeder can rest on the frame tops directly over it. Where double brood chambers are in use and the cluster is occupying the bottom chamber, it is often advisable to remove some of the top chamber combs and place the feeder on the top of the frames in the lower chamber. This extra effort allows the syrup to be in direct contact with the cluster, which is able to make use of it even during the coldest weather. It is an easy matter to quickly lift the feeder when empty, shake off any adhering bees and replace with a full one if required.

A slight leakage may occur when the feeder is first inverted, but this soon ceases as the partial vacuum formed inside is balanced by atmospheric pressure.

Making Syrup

Syrup can be prepared by pouring a quantity of sugar into a suitable container, shaking it level, then noting where the level appears *(Fig. 63)*. Water is then poured in, cold is satisfactory, but hot is better. Stir continuously to release air trapped in the sugar, adding water until the level of the mixture reaches the original level of the sugar *(Fig. 64)*. When dissolved the solution represents approximately 57 per cent sugar to water, which is most suitable for such feeding.

When syrup is liable to remain in the feeders, or if it is to be stored for any length of time, a fungoid, scummy growth may form on the surface and deteriorate the mixture. It is good practice to add a little thymol to syrup when made, which reduces such waste. Thymol does not dissolve readily in water, but a solution can easily be made up, a bottle of which will serve for many years.

One-third fill a four or eight ounce bottle with thymol crystals and top up with surgical alcohol, which quickly dissolves the crystals. Use this solution at a rate of half a teaspoonful to a gallon of syrup.

Sugar syrup, like nectar, is composed of complex sugar and before bees can make full use of it this sugar has to be inverted. During summer the digestive enzymes of many bees complete this change, but in winter, bees fed on sugar syrup are forced to consume it in the "raw" state. Although sugar syrup may keep a colony alive when inactive, it is far from being an ideal food, at this time, the high water-content present often causing dysentery.

Autumn Feeding

After an adverse season, or if the beekeeper has depleted stocks of honey stores too severely, it may be necessary to feed sugar syrup in the autumn.

Fig. 57. *Shaking warm syrup on starving bees in dire emergency.*

Fig. 58. *Miller feeder. Scotch float feeder and round tin feeder.*

Fig. 59. *Seven-pound squat honey tin feeders showing perforated lids.*

Fig. 60. *The honey tin feeder is extremely easy to handle.*

Fig. 61. *Honey tin feeders in position in early spring. Crown board has been removed to ascertain position of cluster.*

Fig. 62. *An old tyre cut longditudinally makes a water fountain. The open trough is filled with wood shavings.*

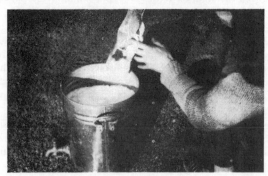

Fig. 63. *Making syrup. Sugar is poured in, shaken level and a note taken of distance from top of container.*

Fig. 64. *Hot water is added until original sugar level is reached. The mixture is agitated until sugar is dissolved.*

Autumn feeding should be given in time for bees to take it down, invert the sugar and store it properly in the combs, otherwise the cluster is forced to exist on "raw" syrup. If given too early a colony may convert such feeding into brood, which could have its advantages in some years. It must be borne in mind, however, that should this occur, the amount of over-winter feeding calculated on might be seriously underestimated.

Usually the month of September is chosen for autumn feeding. At this time of year colonies are strong and temperatures are such as to allow bees access to any type of feeder. The squat honey tin with its perforated lid is still quite suitable for this form of feeding. A number of them can be placed on a stock at one time.

When a goodly amount of syrup has to be fed, the Miller type feeder, which holds about seventeen pints, is very useful, a strong colony being capable of emptying it in one day. This feeder is made to the dimensions of the various hives and has the advantage that no spare chamber is required to box it in. A screen board makes it a useful cover for this feeder. Scotch float feeders, bottle and stage feeders, round tin or plastic, so-called rapid feeders and frame feeders, all have their merits but are unsuitable for use during cold weather and hold such small amounts of syrup that much more labour is entailed when a fair amount of feeding is required (Fig. 58).

It has been suggested that a heavier concentration of syrup is more economical for use in autumn feeding, but to avoid crystallisation in the feeders, the ratio should not exceed twenty pounds of sugar to nine pints of water.

Robbing

Feeding is done at a time when nectar is not coming into the hive, therefore precautions must be taken to prevent robbing. Robbing occurs during a nectar dearth, especially when colonies are of unequal strength, the stronger tending to rob the stores of the weaker (Fig.203). Once begun it is very difficult to control. To prevent its onset, it is advisable to keep only strong stocks in the one apiary, to reduce the entrances of hives when feeding and to avoid spilling or leaving food of any kind exposed in or near the apiary. Various devices are tried to discourage robbing once it has commenced. They include hanging wet or carbolic acid-impregnated cloths over the entrances of the hives being robbed; reducing the entrances of hives to a single bee space; or closing up the affected hives completely for a day or so. Perhaps the best remedy is to remove the affected stocks away from the apiary.

In the past it was suggested that twenty pounds of stores was sufficient to carry an average colony through winter but although this amount may have applied satisfactorily to the old native black bees, a much greater amount is required by the various trains and crosses populating many apiaries to-day. Whilst twenty pounds of stores may see a colony through until February, there is a greater consumption of stores from then onwards, as brood rearing commences.

Stores are required not only to over-winter colonies, but to allow them to expand brood rearing in the spring until such time as reliable outside sources become available. Fifty pounds of stores is generally found to be a satisfactory quantity. In some early seasons a colony may not use this amount, but those surplus stores are not wasted and alleviate risk of starvation until the first spring examination.

It will be noted that a single British standard chamber is hardly large enough to accommodate fifty pounds of stores and still leave space for the winter cluster. In this respect double brood chamber management is superior for wintering.

Assessing the amount of stores in a hive often presents uncertainty. It is dangerous practice to assess the quantity merely by glancing over the tops of the combs, as an examination of a typical brood comb will show that, in many instances, only a thin canopy of honey is present. "Hefting" the hives is the surest method, for if equipment is standardised, the owner can, with a little experience, judge the weights inside. It is advisable to heft each side of the hive in turn and mentally average the combined weight as the stores are often concentrated on one side. A beekeeper with powerful physique can obtain quicker results by grasping the hive under the floorboards with both hands and lifting it slightly off its stance.

Although there are occasions when bees must be fed, it is far better practice and less trouble to the beekeeper to leave enough natural stores on a stock at all times. The weight of stores should not fall below twenty pounds at any time of the year.

If stocks have been put in to winter with adequate stores there is little the beekeeper need do in the apiary until well into the spring months, apart from checking mouse excluders and inspecting the hives after severe gales or flooding. It is impossible to set hard and fast dates for the first examinations, as seasons and regions vary so much, but a useful guide is found in the Flowering Currant. This shrub commences blooming any time from early April till early May, depending on locality and season and when it is in full bloom it may be assumed an opportune time to examine bees, if a suitable day can be chosen. This shrub is easily grown, looks attractive and in an apiary or garden, can serve as a useful "beekeeping barometer". *(Fig.65)*.

During the first examination as little disturbance to the brood nest as possible should be made, as damage through chilling can result and it serves little useful purpose. The object of this examination is to ascertain whether the stock is queen-right, to replace combs if deemed expedient, to "spring-clean" the hive parts, to ensure adequate food is present and to consider what method of supering is required.

After subduing a stock and removing the roof and crown board or cover, it is only necessary to gently prise apart a few combs at the side of the brood nest and partially withdraw a comb likely to contain brood. *(Fig. 66)*. A glance should be sufficient to recognise if the queen is laying satisfactorily and if she is, no further disturbance to the brood nest should be made. Often this information can be gleaned simply by glancing down the combs without having to withdraw one.

If equipment in the apiary is standardised, the hive body should be prised from the floor board and placed on its inverted roof after removing the mouse excluder. A clean floorboard is now placed on the original site and the hive reassembled on the new floorboard. *(Fig. 67)*. The original floor board is then cleaned and scraped free of debris with the hive tool, ready for replacing in the next hive. *(Fig. 68)*.

If any combs requiring replacement are seen to be empty of brood or stores, these can be removed and replaced with new frames of drawn comb prepared in previous years. Cleaning of frame tops and crown board, if necessary completes the operation. *(Fig. 70)*.

Depending on locality and thus on likely sources of early nectar, the food position must then be reviewed. Where no early sources of nectar are available, adequate stores must be present to maintain a colony until such times as fresh supplies are forthcoming. Where the locality is such that early sources could be expected, supering with drawn comb should now be considered.

More Room.

It is widely accepted that one of the principal causes of swarming is congestion of the brood nest, but what is not so generally recognised is that this condition often occurs early in the season and if steps are not taken then, swarms may develop later despite preventative measures adopted by the beekeeper afterwards.

Colonies may commence brood rearing as early as Mid-January when only a few eggs are laid by the queen. If the colony is strong and weather and locality prove favourable, this amount may increase substantially by the end of March. A sufficient number of empty cells is required for this purpose and the subsequent development of the larvae. Equally important, these cells must be in a position where the colony can make use of them.

By April, early nectar and pollen may be available, which, when gathered by forager bees, serves as an invaluable food source, thus hastening colony build-up. In early spring, the bee community confines itself to that part of the hive used for brood rearing and, if available, a small area immediately above it. When space above the brood is lacking, freshly-gathered nectar is often stored in and around the brood nest and as this has a greater volume than when ripened as honey, many cells which would be better utilised for brood rearing merely become storage cells *(Fig. 69)*. Later examinations may not reveal these conditions. The colony, in all probability, would have used up the food in a short space of time for feeding brood. So, too, can this invaluable food source become the means of introducing the germ of swarming fever unless space is made available for storage outwith the brood nest.

The remedy is simple. A super of drawn comb should be provided over the brood chamber. *(Fig. 71)*. If fresh nectar is present in the brood chamber, a comb containing some can be withdrawn and placed in the super, which induces the bees upwards. An uncapped comb of the previous season's honey serves the same purpose.

In apiaries where section honey only is produced the supplying of crates of empty, drawn sections immediately above the brood chambers will provide storage cells for early nectar. Like the beekeeper producing extracted honey, it may rarely be that the section-producer can secure this early nectar in the form of surplus honey, but the provision of storage cells above the brood nest has the most desirable effect of relieving congestion, although it may be but temporary.

Owing to the cold weather and to the limited strength of the colony at this time of year, foundation is of no value, as only completed or partially-completed cells can be used for immediate food storage and wax-secreting bees are unable to provide the high temperature necessary for wax production. Under such conditions, bees nibble away wax foundation and may cover it with propolis varnish, rendering it completely unserviceable.

The use of a queen excluder has the disadvantage of retarding the bees' passage, but is recommended to avoid the risk of having brood reared in the super combs unless a natural barrier in the form of a thick canopy of honey is already present.

The examination of a stock in spring will reveal that the brood nest has been started in the position last occupied by the winter cluster. This position is frequently found to be in the upper part of the hive, the cluster having eaten upwards into its stores following its self-created warmth. Where a double brood chamber is used, this situation can be a disadvantage for, during cold weather, bees are loath to travel downward into the cold belt of air formed in the lower extremities of the hive. Thus throughout part of the season the bottom brood chamber may remain deserted. This waste of space is accentuated in a hive made up of a standard brood chamber with a shallow chamber on top. In such a hive, a colony may adhere to the limited space afforded by the shallow combs and may swarm later through lack of accessible room, although the greater part of the comb area in the hive remains empty.

If noted in the early summer, this condition is easily rectified by switching round the top and bottom chambers so that the empty combs are now positioned on top and thereby made accessible to the bees. To transfer a comb of brood from the brood nest to the empty chamber above will induce the colony to make quicker use of the extra room made available, but this operation should be carried out only with powerful colonies, as premature brood spreading may result in chilled larvae. Where the brood nest is situated between the brood chambers in a double-brood-chambered hive, so that brood is present in both the top and bottom frames, this reversal of chambers should be avoided, as it would split the brood nest, leaving an intervening area of empty comb or stores which the cluster may be unable to bridge. This again may cause chilled brood.

Throughout the active season the extremities of the brood nest are normally bounded by pollen stores. At the sides this takes

26

Fig. 65. Flowering currant—a useful beekeeping "barometer."

Fig. 66. Spring inspection to check stock has ample food and is queenright.

Fig. 67. After subduing, brood chambers are set on upturned roof. Original floor board is replaced by a clean one before re-assembly.

Fig. 68. Floor board is cleaned with hive tool, scraping with grain of wood. It is then ready for next hive.

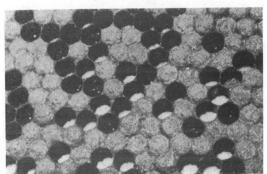

Fig. 69. Nectar stored among brood causes congestion in brood nest.

Fig. 70. Removing brace comb from frame tops.

Fig. 71. Adding queen excluder and super of drawn comb gives storage space above brood rearing area.

Fig. 72. Granulated honey discarded from stock on corrugated iron. Feeding water or thin syrup prevents this.

the form of combs filled almost from top to bottom with tightly-packed pollen. Although invaluable food, these pollen-clogged combs often form a barrier to the queen. The restriction they create can readily be observed in the fifteen-frame hives of the Glen type, where, unless manipulations are carried out, the colony is often seen to occupy, even in mid-summer, only a fraction of the space afforded by such a large hive. This problem presents itself to a lesser degree in the more common ten-frame or eleven-frame hives.

Should the brood nest be restricted in this manner, these pollen combs should be moved outward from their position next to the brood and any empty combs not being utilised in the chamber inserted in their place. It is advisable to carry out these operations in stages, moving the pollen combs outward one frame space at a time, allowing the inserted empty comb to become occupied before shifting the pollen comb a further frame-space along.

It is possible to insert empty combs into the centre of the brood nest, inter-spacing them with combs of brood, but unless the colony is very strong, this incurs the risk of chilled larvae should the temperature fall. An over-abundance of stores carried over from the previous autumn can also restrict breeding space. This is simply rectified by removing some of the surplus honey combs and replacing them with empty ones.

Some beekeepers prefer to have their colonies on combs running the "warm way" i.e. having the brood chambers located on the floor boards so that the combs are parallel to the entrance instead of the more usual method of having them running at right angles to the entrance or the so called "cold way". As far as the colony is concerned either method appears to be satisfactory but it will be noted that in the "warm way", the brood nest tends to be located near the entrance and the stores concentrated at the back of the hive. A situation which prevents easy interchanging of combs and the spreading of pollen clogged combs results.

In some seasons, combs placed the "cold way" simulate the effect of having the stores concentrated at the rear of the hive although in this case the store area is spread over a larger number of combs. Reversing the brood chamber so that its original back faces the entrance, encourages the bees to redistribute their stores and thus leave more accessible room for brood rearing.

To avoid congestion in the brood nest, therefore, super early with drawn comb, provide comb for breeding in accessible places, i.e. above and at the sides and ensure in general that the brood nest is allowed to occupy all available space in the brood chambers if required.

Chapter VIII

Summer Management

Careful attention to winter and spring management does much to cut down labour during the bee-keeper's busiest time and contributes greatly towards securing a good surplus honey return. The advantages of early supering have already been considered and summer management is now a case of ensuring that storage space is always available - in other words - supering in advance of the colonies' requirements, controlling swarming, increasing if required and queen rearing.

Handling Bees

All these operations involve handling bees and perhaps the greatest asset a beekeeper can have is the ability to do this and to recognise the conditions under which it can best be done.

Vicious strains of bees are rare, but can often be reasonably handled by a competent operator. On the other hand, a normally quiet colony can remain troublesome throughout the season due to persistent bad handling.

Choose a Nectar Flow

Bees' temper is undoubtedly influenced by the quantity of fresh nectar available, which in turn is governed by weather and locality. The popular belief that a warm, sunny day between the hours of ten in the morning and four in the afternoon should be chosen to inspect stocks can, in some districts, be completely erroneous. Very often nectar is available in the early morning and again in the evening when the dew points are at their highest. Colonies, easily managed in the morning, have proved difficult when opened around mid-day, even in warm, sunny weather. It is advisable to check up on activity at the hive entrance before stocks are examined and with experience, it is possible to judge whether nectar is coming in. Bees returning with the peculiar hump-backed appearance indicate that their honey crops are full.

Avoid Distasteful Odours

Bees are influenced by scents. Scented haircreams, perspiration, alcohol and especially the scent of horses, appear particularly obnoxious to them.

Dress the Part

Certain colours and materials irritate bees. The wearing of dark clothing such as dark blue dungarees or a dark hat should be avoided. Beekeepers with dark hair, especially those using the offensive haircream, should don a hat before even approaching the apiary. Loose hair is especially annoying and rough woollen material, such as Harris tweed, receives much unwanted attention. Angry bees entwining themselves in such fabric buzz and sting furiously.

Amongst a few beekeepers there exists a feeling of bravado when handling bees. A veil is neither worn nor carried and a good stinging looked upon as an honour. Such practice cannot be too strongly condemned, especially where beginners are present. Although beekeepers should eventually endeavour to discard a veil when conditions are favourable and when they have acquired confidence in their own handling, it should always be carried and when manipulations are necessary during unfavourable conditions, worn when required.

As mentioned, scent can irritate bees and probably none more so than that of a sting. If a colony is restive and a sting is received on the face, it is very likely that within a few moments the area round this first sting will be attacked again. A veil prevents this. Bee gloves, however, can be a deterrent to smooth handling, for even when great care is taken an occasional bee can sting a glove when inadvertently squashed by the operator. This sting may go unnoticed, but shortly afterwards the colony may become aggressive, angry bees stinging round the first affected area and when several stocks have to be examined, the scent of the sting received at the first hive may upset each hive in turn.

Bees have an annoying habit of crawling up sleeves and trouser legs and when pressure is applied, a sting on the forearm, wrist or leg results. To prevent this, an elastic band, or tight-fitting gauntlet should be worn over the sleeves, while the ankles should be protected by gum boots, cycle clips or by tucking the trouser ends into socks.

Handle with Care

In handling bees, use slow, deliberate movements, as sudden jerking motions attract the attentions of guard bees. To this end, well-made hives, with proper spacing and evenly-drawn combs, are advantageous. Judicious use of the hive tool does much to eliminate the wrenching and snapping of propolised combs, which can also tend to upset a colony (Fig. 75).

Proper Subduing

One of the most commonest faults made by the inexperienced is improper subduing. Smoke is generally the most effective agent, although the carbolic cloth can be used to advantage at times. A smoker with a large combusion chamber, which will hold a good amount of proper fuel, is desirable. Corrugated cardboard, often used in the small smoker, burns too hotly and rapidly and is inclined to blow particles of burning material into the hive. Old sacking is suitable fuel and can be inter-rolled with corrugated cardboard to form cartridges. Care should be taken to ensure that sacking used for this purpose has had no contact with any substances harmful to bees.

When smoke is puffed into a hive the guard bees are first of all demoralised and this panic spreads throughout the colony. In their panic, bees rush to cells of honey and commence gorging themselves. A properly subdued colony will reveal that a great number of its inmates have their heads buried in honey cells. It takes a few minutes before the smoke affects the bees throughout the entire colony, and it is not sufficient simply to puff in smoke, then immediately open a hive.

It is important that subduing should be the first part of the operaton (Fig. 73). It so often happens that the beekeeper lights the smoker, sets it down, then lifts off the hive roof for a preliminary examination. The slightest vibration on the hive or around it at times is quite enough to upset a colony, as beekeepers or gardeners who have mowed or hoed the ground round a hive can testify, and this preliminary examination without subduing often ends in a one-sided battle. Returning forager bees are not subdued and when these appear to be causing trouble, a carbolic cloth laid loosely a few inches from the hive entrance will do much to divert their unwelcome advances.

Once the first subduing is carried out it is a mistake to use great volumes of smoke over the tops of the combs, as this serves only to drive bees out the entrance. A gentle puff should be applied to the area of exposed bees, just sufficient to keep them from boiling up if they show signs of doing so.

Some races of bees react to the effects of smoke in varying degrees. The remarks about subduing bee colonies in this book refer mainly to strains of the dark European native bee which are most commonly kept in Scotland and the North of England. Strains of Italian and Carniolan honey bees however, often require much less smoke to subdue them and any slight excess use of smoke sometimes causes "bunching" or "boiling" over the sides of the hive.

There are days when although there are no visible signs of an electric storm, the atmosphere is still and thundery and

Fig. 73. *Subduing stock. Smoke applied at entrance then time given for bees to be properly subdued.*

Fig. 74. *Supers removed and placed on upturned roof.*

Fig. 75. *First roller in position. Frame is loosened with hive tool and placed in box or laid at entrance of hive*

Fig. 76. *Few bees are exposed when two rollers are in operation.*

Fig. 77. *Foundation partially drawn in bottom brood chamber. Comb has been started at top and extended downwards.*

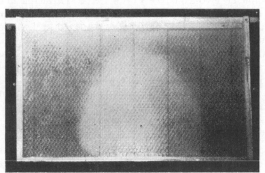

Fig. 78. *Foundation partially drawn in top brood chamber. Comb has been started at bottom and extended upwards.*

Fig. 79. *Typically badly drawn comb from bottom chamber.*

Fig. 80. *Well-drawn comb from top chamber.*

bees can be very aggressive. It is better to leave colony inspections alone on such occasions. A clue is sometimes seen by the presence of small black flies - sometimes called "thunder flies" in the apiary. These can often be spotted, crawling about the hive entrances or alighting on the beekeeper's hand or face.

Tips on Manipulation

When the cover, or crown board, is removed it is advisable to expose as few bees as possible and here the use of rollers is recommended. These are easily made from some smooth, tough material like canvas, cut long enough to cover the entire area of the exposed combs and tacked to a length of wood slightly longer than the breadth of the hive. Two such rollers are used, the first one being placed to cover all the tops of the combs, then as it is rolled back, the second roller is unfurled to cover the combs already examined; thus only one or two combs are exposed at any one time *(Fig. 76)*.

When a major examination involves complete dismantling of a hive, it is always best to start at the bottom. Supers and top brood chamber, if used, are removed and set aside, inverted flat roofs of single-walled hives making ideal stands for the purpose *(Fig. 74)*. Care should be taken to cover the tops of the chambers with a crown board, or other suitable covering. The bottom brood chamber is examined, then the next bottom chamber is placed back in position, examined and so on. This facilitates handling, as it will be found that as each chamber is worked, bees are being driven down to an area already examined.

If the operator starts at the top, bees are continually driven downwards until at length, when the bottom chamber is reached, it will be crowded with bees, which are apt to boil over and are more difficult to control.

The siting of stocks plays an important part in easy manipulation and consideration should be given to the remarks on setting out an apiary.

To sum up, choose suitable weather and time if possible; wear light-coloured, smooth clothing; avoid annoying scents; gain confidence so as to handle firmly and smoothly; give time for colonies to be properly subdued, and the handling of bees becomes a greater pleasure both to beekeeper and bees.

The Foundation of Good Combs

In the modern moveable frame hive, evenly and well drawn comb is essential for ease of manipulation and good management. Although sugar syrup feeding can be restored to for drawing combs, much better results are obtained during a good nectar flow.

The term, "drawing of combs", may be a trifle misleading, as when wax foundation is inserted into a stock, bees make partial use of the wax supplied, but also add wax secreted by themselves to form the familiar hexagonal-shaped cells of the comb. The high temperature necessary for wax secretion is governed by weather, strength of colony and the location of secreting bees within the hive. The area immediately above the brood nest appears to be most attractive for this purpose. Foundation is more readily accepted and drawn in this position.

The introduction of wax foundation to a stock under unfavourable conditions often results in its being coated with propolis varnish and when thus treated, bees are loath to draw it out. Instead, they are apt to nibble it away, or attach brace comb to it by waxen supports. "Brace comb" is a term applied to pieces of natural comb built in odd places in a hive. Such propolised foundation is termed "stale" and should be discarded, including section foundation left over from a previous year, if any glaze or signs of travel-stainng are seen.

Many unsightly or wasted sections of honey are the direct result of misguided economy in trying to use up such stale foundation.

Good combs are seldom drawn in a single-brood chamber, unless by a powerful swarm during a heavy nectar flow. When frames of foundation are inserted into a single-brood chamber, the cells are generally drawn from the top of the frame downwards *(Fig. 77)* so that, before the foundation at the bottom of the frame is started, it is liable to become travel-stained, or covered with propolis and is subsequently nibbled down. Although only a strip of comb from a quarter to one inch is lost, the resultant space between the bottom of the comb and the wooden rails of the frame makes the task of finding a queen bee much more difficult. *(Fig. 79)*.

A beekeeper wishing to adhere strictly to single-brood chamber management can obtain well-drawn standard combs by using them in a deep chamber above a queen excluder. When properly drawn, filled and sealed, these deep combs are removed and the honey carefully extracted. These empty combs are then ready for insertion into a brood chamber.

In double-brood chamber management, brood combs can be satisfactorily drawn out in the top chamber, or if desired, in the form of a super above a queen excluder.

When frames of foundation are being drawn above the brood nest, whether they are in a top brood chamber or super, the bottom of the comb is generally started first and the process expands in an upward direction *(Fig. 78)*. This results in the comb being built hard agains the bottom rails of the frame, so that no space is created where a queen could lurk and as the last of the foundation is at the top, it is removed from travel-staining or propolising to a great extent *(Fig. 80)*.

Foundation, stored for a period, especially thin super used in sections, may present a hard, brittle appearance, which, once again, is not ideal for good comb building. This dryness, caused by the evaporation of the essential oils on the wax surface, can be remedied by gently warming in front of a fire, or exposing it to strong sunlight. This softens the surface and allows the essential oils to penetrate to the exterior, making it more acceptable to the bees. When handling frames with new foundation affixed, they should not be laid on their sides on the flat, as the heat of the sun may cause the wax to soften and the foundation to bulge. This, of course, tends to cause uneven combs.

Spacing is also important. Where metal ends are used, foundation started off on wide metal ends tends to be drawn unevenly and brace comb may be built between the sheets of foundation. Narrow metal ends should be used for such frames; alternatively, wide ones staggered so that eleven bars can fit into a single-walled hive super.

Metal ends are so designed as to give a space between foundation and foundation to allow bees to draw out comb and to leave a bee space between completed comb and comb. However, the end frames in a chamber present a problem, as the narrow metal end coming in contact with the end wall of the hive restricts this space.It is often found that the inside surface of the foundation is drawn, but the external surface ignored, as the bees cannot cluster properly in this limited space. Such combs are frequently seen having one side perfectly well drawn, while on the other a propolised surface of foundation remains. Later, a heavy nectar flow may develop when the stock is extremely populous and the overflow of bees may build comb in this area, but as the foundation has been propolised, seldom will this comb be drawn properly and an area of brace comb is built either on the wall of the hive itself, or on waxen supports from the old foundation. Thin fillets of wood can be inserted between the wall of the hive and the outside narrow metal ends, or if preferred, wide metal ends may be used on the outside frames, which space the foundation the proper distance from the hive wall, allowing ample space for clustering and drawing comb.

A colony will often neglect the outside frames of foundation and draw the centre of a chamber. Where this is observed during a honey flow it is advisable to alter the positions of the combs by placing the drawn ones to the outside and moving the undrawn ones from the outside to the centre, providing no brood is present. This ensures an evenly drawn chamber.

In modern apiculture, the trend is for all combs to be started on worker foundation and if these are drawn properly, each comb should consist almost entirely of worker cells. Certainly, the conception that an over-abundance of drones being a liability is sound, but the elimination of drone breeding opposes the natural instincts of a honey bee colony and cannot reasonably be prevented altogether. A colony housed on perfect worker cell combs tends to nibble some of these cells back to the foundation and build drone cells in their place. This point can be demonstrated in a powerful colony housed on well-drawn worker comb, where normally any brace comb built will be of drone cells, whereas a nucleus or a weak colony usually builds brace comb of worker cells.

Combs requiring replacement should be gradually moved towards the extremity of the brood chamber, where they are most likely to emptied of both brood and stores. In this position they are often found empty at the spring examination, when they can be removed and replaced.

An adaptation of the Demaree method is most useful when a large number of combs in the one hive require replacing. The queen is confined in a new chamber set above a queen excluder over the original combs, so that after three weeks all brood has hatched from the unwanted combs which can be removed at leisure. All that is necessary is to shake the bees from the old combs and reassemble the hive.

Discretion should be exercised when selectng combs for retention or discard. It will be seen that although a surfeit of drone cells is undesirable, combs containing patches of such cells may prove an asset as their presence tends to discurage an excess building of brace comb. Combs not being fully utilised, due to bad drawing, proplised foundation or damage caused by rough handling, mice or fungoid growths, should be replaced.

A beekeeper should have no difficulty in ensuring that his colonies are suitably housed if periodic examinations are made to weed out undesirable combs and care taken at the outset to ensure they are propely drawn.

Supering

Adding honey supers to producing stocks is not a complicated manipultion once a sufficient stock of drawn comb has been made available for the purpose. A super is best placed on the top of a previous one, especially if foundation has to be drawn, and should be added when the previous super is approximately two-thirds full.

There is a possible exception in the case of section honey production where a new section crate is often inserted beneath the previous one when it is almost full and sealed. The reason for this is to prevent travel-staining on the finished sections. There is a hazard here, however, as bees do not leave empty spaces when forming their storage area. If a heavy nectar flow continued, the space created might be utilised satisfactorily, but if the nectar flow be intermittent, or cease altogether, there is every chance of the honey being removed from the filled supers and partially transferred to the empty area below. This may give very patchy results, which makes extracting more tedious and, in the case of sections, could spoil the appearance of an otherwise marketable crop. Foundation in such circumstances could readily become propolised and rendered useless.

Although it is good practice to give a colony ample storage in advance of its requirements, thus relieving congestion in the brood chamber, a certain amount of discretion must be used. If a new super is added prematurely, or at the tail-end of a nectar flow, the stock has a tendency to "chimney" i.e the storage space is confined to one part of all the supers to the neglect of the remaining space. This occurs most frequently in the centre combs of supers where the outer combs are neglected. Such a condition is in no way detrimental to the colony, the only objections being the extra work involved when extracting and the employment of more equipment than is necessary *(Fig. 153)*.

A new super appears to be occupied more readily if a comb or two of open honey is introduced to it from the previously filled super, the inter-changing of combs being a simple operation. Again, experience and intimate knowledge of locality determine the timing of providing additional supering space.

Cherchez La Femme

One of the operations involved in many beekeeping manipulations is that of finding the queen bee and although this generally can only be easily accomplished after considerable experience, certain routine aids can be employed to advantage. During beekeeping operations the presence of a nectar flow aids the operator and in this case, the many field bees outwith the hive leave the combs less crowded.

In a single-brood chamber hive the minimum amount of smoke should be used in subduing, otherwise the queen is apt to run to any part of the brood chamber where she may not be readily spotted. After the supers and queen excluder have been removed,one or two outer combs are taken from the brood chamber, examined, then placed in a nucleus or small travelling box set at the side of the hive *(Fig. 81)*. It is helpful to look for evidence of the queen's whereabouts rather than for the queen herself. To explain this, picture the extreme example of an outside comb filled with stores. It would be most unlikely to find a queen here! A comb containing eggs is where a queen is more likely to be and the one which should be given very close scrutiny.

Keeping this in mind, the remainder of the frames are now examined and replaced in the hive in their original order.

With experience, the majority of queens are found by the following method.

The operator takes up a stance at one side of the hive, preferably with his back to the sun, so that the exposed face of the combs can be viewed while they are still in the hive. As one comb is removed, it is held in the hands, swung to one side, but not examined immediately. Instead, the eyes should focus on the face of the next comb exposed in the hive *(Fig. 82)*. If the queen is on that face she will readily be seen running towards the bottom of the comb away from the light, her long abdomen, in that position, singling her out. On seeing her, the operator should quickly set down the comb in his hands and remove that on which the queen was seen.

If the queen is not discovered on this exposed face of comb in the hive, the comb held in the hands should now be examined systematically. On occasions when bees cluster thickly on the comb, the queen may remain concealed underneath. The cluster must be broken up in this case and although gentle smoking can be employed, a better method is to use the fingers in a gentle patting motion. Bees quickly disperse under this slight pressure *(Fig. 83)*.

Once all the combs have been examined as described and the queen has still not been seen, the operator should take up a stance on the other side of the hive and repeat the routine.

Should a second examination not reveal the queen and it is imperative to find her, continue in this manner or consider some drastic measures. One such measure is to shake all the bees on to an alighting board and to keep careful watch for the queen as she runs towards the hive. Another is to space half the number of combs in an empty chamber in pairs. As the queen tends to evade light she can sometimes be found on the inside surface of a pair of combs after a lapse of about ten minutes.

In the writer's opinion, if the queen is not found on the second examination of the brood combs, the best course is to close up the hive and re-examine later.

During the confusion of separating combs, young queens especially may run in front of the operator and are sometimes found on the very last comb to be examined in the chamber. A virgin queen is apt to escape notice because of her movements, which, unlike those of a mated queen, are very quick. A mated queen is more readily spotted as she is normally surrounded by her retinue of workers, whose heads point toward her *(Fig. 84)*.

Should a queen take to the air during an examination, the hive should be left open, with the frame tops exposed, as the scent from the colony will encourage her to return.

Double-Brood Chamber Technique

Here a slight variation is used to find the queen. It may seem surprising that a queen can often be more easily located in such a large brood area. This is because the bees have more room to spread out and therefore do not tend to cluster so tightly as in a single-brood chamber.

Smoke a double-brood chamber hive at the entrance heavily for a few minutes then remove the supers and top brood chamber as quickly as possible. Two hive roofs make ideal stands, one for the supers and the other for the top brood chamber. The heavy smoking drives the queen upwards and if brood is present in both chambers, she is almost certain to be found in the top chamber. The queen is often trapped on the queen excluder, so examine it carefully when removing. *(Fig. 85)*.

The value of properly drawn combs can be seen to advantage during this operation and marked queens, of course, are much easier to detect.

Marking the Queen

Queen bees should not be marked early in the season and much care is required in their handling. The various queen-marking paints on the market are quite satisfactory and unless the beekeeper wishes to experiment at the risk of losing a few queens, other marking substances should not be used. Marking paint should be applied to the back of the queen's thorax directly from the nozzle of tubed paint, or from the tip of a match dipped in the marking substance.

"TRI CHEM" paint used for liquid embroidery can be obtained in suitable ball point nozzled tubes and has proved extremely successful. The nozzle of this container shold be pressed on a hard surface such as a hive tool until a small puddle of the paint is formed, then the paint-charged nozzle is applied gently to the queen's thorax. White or yellow colouring is more readily observed amongst the darkness of the combs.

The various "holding-down" cages are very useful and should be used by a beginner, or by a person whose sight or steadiness of hand is unreliable *(Fig. 86)*. The orthodox method of picking a queen up by her wings, using the thumb and forefinger of the right hand, then transferring her to the left hand, where she is gently held by her thorax between thumb and forefinger, requires confidence and practice, but is successfully performed by many beekeepers. The writer's preference is to catch the queen against a patch of soft comb afforded by open brood or unsealed honey, by using the thumb and forefinger held together to form a fork. As the weight of the hand is mainly resting on the comb, greater steadiness and manoeuvrability is achieved.

Before marking the queen, she should be caught from behind and held gently by the thorax. In this position the top of her thorax is readily accessible for the application of marking paint *(Fig. 87)*.

Clipping a queen's wing is an aid to swarm control. To do this she should be caught from the front and again held by the thorax, as in this position the wings are exposed *(Fig. 88)*. It is sufficient to cut one large wing on one side down to the size of a small wing. This throws the insect off balance should she endeavour to fly. Cutting alternate wings according to year of birth is a means of checking ages of queens.

A queen should never be handled by her abdomen as her reproductive organs are easily damaged.

Queen Balling

A queen bee is sometimes "balled", which means that worker bees attack her and while not directly attempting to kill her, form themselves into a ball with the queen in the centre. Thus she is deprived of food and air and often dies as a result.

Balling can be attributed to two main causes - disturbance too early in the season and the acquiring of a strange scent. This scent can originate from the beekeeper, who may use highly-scented soap or handle chemicals. Cigarette smokers should bear this point in mind.

If possible, marking and clipping a queen should be carried out during a nectar flow when the likelihood of balling is most remote.

Occasionally a handled queen goes into a state of cataplectic shock and seems to be completely devoid of life. If returned to the comb amongst her daughters and kept quiet and in darkness for half-an-hour or so, she will recover and appear none the worse for her ordeal. This "playing possum" is probably a defense mechanism to protect the most important individual in the colony.

Fig. 81. *Outer comb removed from hive to suitable box.*

Fig. 82. *Searching for queen. Stance at side of hive. Comb is removed, swung to one side then face of comb still in hive is scanned.*

Fig. 83. *When bees cluster tightly on comb, they can be dispersed by gentle patting.*

Fig. 84. *A fertile queen can often be spotted by position of her retinue.*

Fig. 85. *The top brood chamber is removed and examined first in a double brood chamber hive to locate queen.*

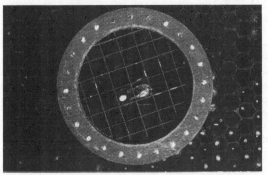

Fig. 86. *A marked queen in "holding-down cage."*

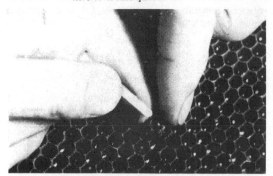

Fig. 87. *The queen is trapped from behind thorax for marking position.*

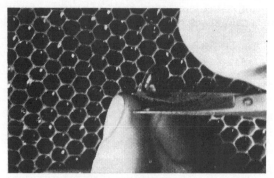

Fig. 88. *The queen is trapped by front of thorax for wing clipping.*

Chapter IX

Swarming And Swarm Control

Different forms of life have various ways of reproducing, from the lowly amoeba, which multiplies by simple division, to the vastly complicated process of the higher mammals in the development from the fertilised egg, through the embryo stages to the form of the parents.

The honey bee is a social insect and as such, is only a part of a community, unable to survive for long away from it. A honeybee could be likened to a cell in the human body. Body cells are continually multiplying, dying and reproducing, but no matter how much they may do so, it can scarcely be said that the body is reproducing itself in the sense that it is propagating the species.

Honey bees do propagate the species by division or by swarming, as it is commonly called. If we imagine a strawberry plant, omitting reproduction by seeding for the moment, we can visualise how division occurs when the plant throws runners. These runners grow from the original plant, root themselves and are then able to maintain a separate existence, plant, omitting reproduction by seeding for the moment, we numerous cells multiplying and dying continually and prospers or fails, each according to its environment. A colony of bees can be compared to one of these plants when it swarms, the parent colony and the swarm existing as two separate units and the individual bees in them multiplying and dying like the cells in the plants.

Swarm Preparations

Let us follow the sequence of events occurring when a colony of honey bees prepares to swarm without interference from a beekeeper.

Queen cell cups are first of all constructed in various parts of the hive, but tending to be concentrated in the centre of the brood nest. Eggs are laid in them over a period of several days and on hatching, the larvae are fed lavishly on royal jelly until being sealed over on the ninth or tenth day from when the eggs were laid. Over this period the queen has slackened her egg laying throughout the hive, which has the effect of reducing the size of her ovaries and rendering her more capable of flying.

Any time after the first queen cell has been sealed over and if weather conditions are favourable, excitement in the colony rises and the bees fill their honey sacs from the cells in the hive.

The Swarm

Within a short time the majority of the flying bees pour "en masse" from the entrance, clamber over the face of the hive and take to the air. As more bees leave the hive the cloud thickens and the tendency is for the bees to hover about facing the direction of the hive. The queen bee does not lead out the swarm; indeed, frequently she is among some of the last to leave.

The encircling bees generally drift in a cloud to some nearby projection, such as a branch of a tree or shrub, where some bees alight and commence exposing the scent gland and fanning. This scent concentration attracts the flying bees to the spot, where they twine themselves together to form a compact cluster. At this juncture scout bees leave the swarm and search for a likely place for a new home, returning to the cluster and imparting the information through the bee dance. The cluster remains intact for anything from a few hours to several days, before once again taking to the air and flying at speeds varying from a fast walking pace up to 15 miles per hour to the new abode.

On arrival, the new home is cleared of debris, wax combs are built, the honey taken from the old hive being used for this, the queen commences egg laying and so a new colony is born.

It sometimes happens that scout bees search in advance of the swarm leaving the hive, in which case the swarm may omit forming a cluster, and fly directly to the new home.

The Parent Stock

Meantime the old stock, or parent stock as it is termed, settles down to redistribute the balance of its labour force. The queen cells mature and after five or six days from when they were sealed over, commence to hatch. When the first virgin queen emerges from her cell, one of two things can happen. She is either permitted to destroy her unborn sisters in the remaining queen cells, which she does by attacking the weaker side walls of the cells and stinging the pupae inside, or she is prevented from doing this and the colony swarms again, this time headed by the virgin queen. This swarm, termed a cast swarm, is normally much smaller than the original, which is known as a prime swarm.

It will be remembered that the eggs originally in the queen cell cups were laid over a period of several days and therefore mature at different times, thus the virgin queens, if not destroyed, emerge over a period. As time passes more virgins hatch and depending on weather, locality, strain and strength of the colony, several cast swarms may issue from the hive until only one queen is left to eventually mate and become the new mother of the colony. Given opportunity, each cast swarm will have its queen mated in time and thus more colonies are created.

It may happen that more than one virgin queen emerges from her cell at the same time, in which case a battle royale ensues, the victor stinging her rival to death with the long, unbarbed sting possessed by queen bees. Unlike the worker's barbed sting, which would probably be left in the body of the vanquished queen, the sting of a queen can be withdrawn. It may also happen that during a suitable day several virgin queens hatch together and emerge with the one cast swarm, but after settling into the new abode, the queens continue their battle for survival until only one is left.

During the time virgin queens are present in a hive a curious, high-pitched piping noise is often heard, which is thought to emanate from the queens challenging each other.

Swarming, therefore, is a perfectly natural occurrence and is the result of the honey bee's instinctive urge to propagate the species. It will be appreciated, however, that if allowed to develop unchecked, honey production would suffer, as the original stock could be so depleted as to become a liability.

Securing the Swarm

If a natural swarm emerges, some measure must be applied to prevent it absconding. Where the swarm has alighted in an accessible position, it is an easy matter to shake it into a suitable container, such as a straw skep, an empty hive, or even a wood or cardboard box, *(Fig. 89),* which should then be inverted over a board and kept shaded. If this is done fairly soon after the swarm has emerged and before scout bees have determined the location of an alternative new site, the cluster will generally reform in the container.

The swarm may have alighted on some projection not readily shaken, such as a firmly-embedded fence post. Here it is an easy matter to invert the container over the top of the post and by means of smoker, carbolic cloth, or manipulaton, drive the bees upward into the receptacle.

Fig. 89. Swarm in accessible position is shaken directly into suitable container.

Fig. 90. Swarm in awkward position requires different tactics.

Fig. 91. A handful or cupful of bees is taken from swarm cluster.

Fig. 92. The removed bees are thrown firmly down beside some suitable container.

Fig. 93. The thrown bees extend abdomen, expose Nasenoff organ and commence fanning.

Fig. 94. The swarm is smoked so that it takes to the air.

Fig. 95. The fanning bees start to attract the flying bees to them.

Fig. 96. The swarm has now deserted original position and reformed cluster in and around container.

Using the "Nasenoff" Organ

It frequently happens that a swarm clusters into some inaccessible position, such as inside a hedge, or among coils of barbed wire, where a container cannot be suitably placed. *(Fig. 90)*. Here the beekeeper can make use of the Nasenoff or scent organ of the bees.

The container is placed near the swarm, inverted over a board and propped up to allow an entrance of a few inches in height. This method has been known to work satisfactorily over fifty feet away, but the nearer the container is to the swarm the better.

A handful, or cupful of bees is secured from the swarm and thrown firmly down on the board at the entrance to the container *(Figs. 91 and 92)*. Bees handled in this way normally commence fanning and exposing the scent organ *(Fig. 93)*. The cluster is then broken up through the use of the smoker and agitation and forced to take wing *(Fig. 94)*. The smoker should be used freely, but not to stupefy the bees, its sole purpose being to get the bees into the air and prevent their settling away from the container.

Alighted bees only can expose the scent organ and flying bees are thus attracted to the container, where the captured bees were placed. This operation may appear spectacular to an onlooker, but it is surprising how often it can be done easily and with success *(Figs. 95 and 96)*.

A point to note is that if a wind is blowing, the shaken bees should be placed upwind from the original swarm cluster so that the scent from the fanning bees wafts in the desired direction.

Hiving the Swarm

The time-honoured method of hiving a swarm is still practised and provides a very interesting spectacle. This is a legacy from the days when bees were kept in skeps and when a beekeeper was afforded his only chance of seeing the queen bee.

A hive prepared with comb is set in position and a hiving board made of plywood, or a substitute such as a large, flattened, cardboard carton, is placed in position resting against the floorboard. Care should be taken that no gap exists at this junction through which a queen could disappear. The board should slope upwards towards the hive and it may be necessary to raise the hive temporarily on bricks for this purpose *(Fig. 97)*. Some prefer to cover the board with a white sheet, giving better foothold for the surging mass of bees and making the queen easier to spot.

The swarm cluster is now lowered gently over the hiving board, then with a sharp jerk, dislodged from the container *(Fig. 98)*. It is fascinating to watch how the mass of bees gradually fans out like a widening pool of oil after falling on the board. Generally within a few minutes some bees start running up into the hive and once this initial move is made, the remainder very quickly follow. It is, of course, desirable to ensure that the queen enters the hive and to this end a stance should be taken up at the side of the hiving board. Usually the queen is quickly spotted, *(Fig. 99)*, but if the bees are inclined to bunch, a slight patting motion with the hand wll break up knots of bees amongst which the queen may be hidden.

A simpler, quicker, but equally effective method is to remove two or three combs from the hive, bump in the swarm from the top, an empty super making a useful funnel, and gently replace the combs once the bees have spread themselves out *(Fig. 100)*.

Unless stores are supplied in the hive and a nectar dearth follows, it will, of course, be necessary to resort to feeding and an examination after a week or so will determine whether the queen has commenced laying. To prevent cast swarms issuing from the parent hive, all queen cells which may be present should be destroyed, leaving only one to eventually hatch out and thus re-queen the colony.

When increase of stocks is not desired, or if no spare hive is available, there are alternative methods of dealing with the swarm. One is to destroy all the queen cells in the parent stock and reunite the swarm with it, at the same time endeavouring to give more room in the brood chamber by removing any combs not containing brood. This method may work satisfactorily, but cannot always be relied upon, the colony sometimes swarming again even although no sealed queen cells are left.

Another method is to remove the queen from the swarm, destroy all queen cells in the parent stock except one and again reunite the swarm with the parent stock. This method generally prevents further swarming, but results in a weakening of the stock in bees. A serious time lag of several weeks is created until such time as the young queen hatches, mates and commences laying.

Swarm Control - Nine-Day Inspection

In modern beekeeping few beekeepers can devote time to chasing and securing natural swarms, but fortunately a satisfactory form of swarm control has been devised. From observations at the hive entrance it is sometimes possible to determine the date of a likely emergence a few days beforehand. One indication is clustering and inactivity at the hive entrance *(Fig. 103)*. These outward observations, however, are not always reliable, nor do they give sufficient warning to the beekeeper.

There was a popular belief that if stocks were examined periodically and any developing queen cells destroyed, the colony could not raise a mature queen cell and would not swarm. Unfortunately this does not always have the desired results and the colony may still swarm in such circumstances even although no sealed queen cell is present. Colonies having made swarm preparations, even to the extent of sealing queen cells, sometimes tear these cells down and appear to give up all further attempts at swarming. This behaviour is most common when a heavy nectar flow develops after a prolonged period of poor conditions. Unfortunately the beekeeper cannot foretell these events and for practical purposes it may be said that the presence of developing queen cells indicates swarming in the colony concerned *(Fig. 102)*.

The term "swarm control" has by common usage become to mean "examining for swarming preparations" and merely indicates to the beekeeper the possibility of impending swarming in the colony concerned. It does not in itself prevent swarming.

The apidictor apparatus, which amplifies noises made by bees, may have great possibilities, but at present there is only one reliable method of swarm control in general use. It is the nine-day inspection.

To understand the principle behind this inspection let us re-examine the development of the queen larva and the sequence of events prior to swarming.

Say on 1st June a colony is examined and is found to have neither queen cells nor queen cell cups with eggs or larvae in them, it would be safe to assume that queen cells could not be sealed over until at least sometime after 9th June. It takes over nine days from when the egg was laid for any bee larvae to reach the sealing-over stage. As a colony does not normally swarm until a queen cell is sealed over, it follows that the colony would not swarm until after 9th June.

If examination on 9th June revealed that still no eggs or larvae were present in queen cells, it would then be safe to assume that the colony would not swarm until sometime after 18th June, and so on.

Queen cell cups, provided they are empty, indicate little, as colonies without swarming intent frequently build many of them. These cups should be left intact, otherwise new cups may be formed in a less obvious position and may be overlooked on a subsequent examination. This is especially applicable in double-brood chamber management.

Fig. 97. *Hive set on stand with sloping hiving board ready for hiving swarm.*

Fig. 98. *The swarm is dumped on to the hiving board.*

Fig. 99. *The Queen is spotted as she crosses the threshold.*

Fig. 100. *A simple way of hiving a swarm. Bees are dumped in at the top using an empty super as a funnel.*

Fig. 101. *The swarm stock is examined a week or so later to ensure queen right.*

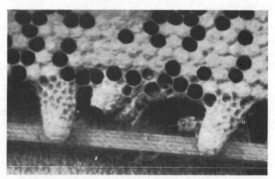

Fig. 102. *The formation of queen cells gives the beekeeper a measure of control.*

Fig. 103 *Clustering at hive entrance is also a clue prior to swarming.*

Fig. 104. *Swarm returning to hive after discovering queen was not with it. The beekeeper had clipped her wing beforehand.*

In single-brood chamber management the procedure is firstly to subdue the colony, remove the roof, supers and queen excluder before carefully examining each comb for signs of developing queen cells (Fig. 105). In a single populous brood chamber it may at times be necessary to shake most of the bees off each comb to expose the brood underneath. If no developing queen cells are seen, either with eggs or larvae, the hive is closed up and a note taken of findings. Apart from ensuring there is adequate room for storing honey in the supers, further attention is not required for nine days. Some beekeepers employ the technique of tipping up the single-brood chamber on the back of the floor board, parting the combs slightly with the hive tool, then after smoking bees from between the frames in the middle of the chamber, ascertaining by glancing between the combs the state of any queen cells present. Because the majority of queen cells tend to develop near the centre of the brood nest, observation from this source is somewhat limited (Figs. 106 and 107).

Perhaps the greatest asset in double-brood chamber management is the simplified examination for swarm control and the saving of labour when time is invaluable. Although a double-brood chamber has 20 or 22 combs, it is not generally necessary to examine all of them; indeed, if properly managed, individual combs are not examined at all. As was stated, queen cells develop near the centre of the brood nest so that if it extends into two chambers and a central cross-section examined, an indication of swarm preparations could be given. This cross-section is easily observed when the double-brood chambers are separated and the bottom of the top chamber examined.

The procedure is again first of all to subdue the colony with smoke then to remove the roof. If the supers are well filled and heavy it will be necessary to remove them one at a time and place them on the upturned roof, but if empty or fairly light, they can be left in position. The use of lock slides assists greatly in this latter operaton, preventing the supers from slipping about.

Working from either the back or front of the hive, the hive tool is inserted at a corner between the double-brood chambers, one hand being used to take the weight off the top chamber and a slight leverage applied, sufficient to break the seal of propolis and brace comb, if present. Still taking the weight off the top chamber on one arm, the hive tool is used to loosen and prise down one at a time any combs in the bottom chamber which may be sticking to the top ones. When all combs are loosened, the top chamber is tipped up slightly and drawn forward about an inch before being hinged up from the back on the bottom chamber. If the chamber is not drawn forward there is a risk of it slipping off the back when being hinged upward.

When in this hinged-back position the bottoms of the top chamber combs can be readily examined. Usually in the active season a number of queen cell cups will be present, either built from the wood rail on the bottom of the frames, or on the comb just above the rails and these should be inspected minutely. It is sometimes an advantage to break down the side walls of a few likely-looking cups with the corner of the hive tool to ascertain if eggs are present and if carefully done, the cell cups will be repaired by the bees before the next examination. As before, if no eggs or larvae are present in these cups, it can be taken for all practical purposes that the colony is not making preparations to swarm and the hive can be reassembled and left unattended for nine days. (Figs 108-112).

There are a few precautions to take using this method. It must be established that the brood nest is indeed extended into the top chamber, as, with a weak stock, or in an adverse year, colonies may restrict the brood nest to the bottom chamber. In these circumstances such an examination is quite useless being comparable to examining the underside of a honey super. It is advisable to peer up between the combs in the top brood chamber, if necessary parting the frames slightly, to verify if brood is present.

Should brood not be present, it will be necessary to remove this top chamber and examine the bottom one, in the same manner as for a stock housed in a single-brood chamber hive.

Clipped Queens.

When a colony with a clipped queen is allowed to swarm naturally, the cluster of bees usually forms in the normal way, but the queen, being unable to fly, is prevented from joining them. Although she is able to leave the hive, the queen frequently is unable to return and falls to the ground where she is often surrounded by a small knot of bees. The queen may perish, but the swarm cluster, realising their state of queenlessness, returns to the hive (Fig. 104) and thus, although the colony may be queenless for some time, the potential foraging force is kept intact. It should not be thought, however, that clipping the queen's wing will prevent swarming indefinitely; this operation only delays the decampment of the swarm.

Let us imagine what would happen after a colony had swarmed, lost its queen and returned to the hive. Numerous queen cells would be present and when one of them hatched, the new virgin queen would likely emerge not only with the original prime swarm, but also with a force of bees which normally would have formed the second or cast swarm and the stock would be even more depleted in foraging strength.

What, then, are the advantages of clipping the queen? A queen cell takes 15-16 days to mature from the time the egg was laid and, therefore, at least that time for a virgin queen to emerge, thus the times between examinations for swarm control can be extended from nine days to fourteen days. This time extension may prove invaluable to the beekeeper who can only attend at his charges at weekends, or who runs out-apiaries at some considerable distance away, an examination being made every second week.

Many beekeepers take the double precaution of both clipping queens and carrying out the routine nine-day inspection, which allows reasonable time to take measures should evidence of swarming be seen.

Fig. 105. *Brood comb being examined for formation of queen cells.*

Fig. 106. *Tilting single brood chamber on its floor board.*

Fig. 107. *View of bottom of combs in tilted single brood chamber. This method is not always reliable.*

Fig. 108. *Double brood chamber splitting. The stock is subdued.*

Fig. 109. *Top chamber lifted slightly. Sticking frames in bottom pushed down with hive tool. Top chamber pulled forward an inch or so.*

Fig. 110. *Top chamber is "hinged" at back and lifted. Smoke is blown to drive bees from area. Lock slides prevent super slipping.*

Fig. 111. *Bottoms of the top chamber combs are examined. Doubtful cell cups are partly broken down to expose any eggs present.*

Fig. 112. *A book entry saves time and unnecessary labour at a later date.*

Chapter X

The Treatment of Swarming Colonies

Factors Affecting Swarming.

The numerous factors which influence the swarming impulse in honey bee colonies include weather, locality, race or strain of bee, age or condition of queen and the form of management practised by the beekeeper.

Weather and locality affect nectar secretion and it is generally agreed that swarming is more prevalent when intermittent nectar flows occur.

Some races and strains of bees are more prone to swarming than others. As swarming is the natural way of reproduction, honey bees do not differ from other forms of life in this respect. The various breeds of poultry and varieties of grain illustrate this. For honey production it is more convenient to maintain a strain of bee not given to excessive swarming and much can be achieved by selective queen rearing.

The work on queen substance by Dr. Butler has done much to throw light on the pattern of bee behaviour in relation to the condition of the queen and this knowledge may yet prove to be a valuable tool in the hands of the practical beekeeper.

Various forms of management can do much to prevent conditions arising which are conducive to swarming. These can be summed up briefly as follows: preventing congestion in the brood nest by early supering; providing supering space in advance of the colonies' requirements; periodic re-queening; and ensuring that ample room for expansion is present in the brood chambers.

Depending on locality, examinations for swarm control should commence at the beginning of May in early southern regions and from the beginning of June in later regions. In most years the swarming impulse is over by the end of July, but beekeepers migrating to late sources, such as heather, with stocks not headed by the current year's queens, would be advised to examine until well into August.

If swarm control by the nine-day inspection reveals no development in queen cells, the beekeeper's lot is an easy one, but when developing queen cells are seen, indicating possible impending swarming, the question arises as to what measures can be adopted to best advantage. The many methods and variations of treating swarming colonies are based on the principle of separating the queen and flying bees from the remainder of the colony; in other words, creating an artificial swarm. Most of these methods take advantage of the fact that flying bees return to the location of their hive and not necessarily to the hive itself.

To illustrate this point, let us observe what happens when a hive is simply shifted a few feet to one side of its site stance. It will be found that returning forager bees appear confused and are apt to circle the original site of the hive for some time before eventually finding the entrance of the hive in its new position. If another hive is placed on the site of the original one, the returning bees tend to treat it as their own and enter it, thus a process of deliberate drifting of bees is implemented.

Pagden

Perhaps the simplest way of dealing with a colony showing the development of queen cells is by the Pagden method. A new hive is placed beside the stock to be treated, its brood chamber filled with either frames of foundation or drawn combs. After subduing the colony and removing the roof, supers and queen excluder, the brood chamber is examined until the queen is found. If she is on a comb of sealed brood, this comb, with the queen, is removed and placed in the new hive, care being taken to destroy any queen cells which may be present on this comb *(Fig. 113)*. Should the queen be on a comb containing eggs or young larvae, it is an easy matter to hold a comb of sealed brood above and against it, then, with a little smoke or hand manipulation, drive the queen upwards onto the sealed brood.

The parent hive is now removed to another site in the apiary *(Fig. 116)* the queen excluder and supers being placed on the new hive, which is then lifted onto the site previously occupied by the parent hive *(Figs. 114-115)*. Bees returning from the field will enter the new hive and join up with those in the supers and the queen, while many bees flying from the parent hive will return to the original site and again add to the strength of what is virtually a swarm of bees. It is desirable to choose a day when bees are flying freely for this manipulation, although it is possible, with experience, to shake bees from the parent hive into the new one during inclement weather conditions. This latter course must be very carefully considered however, as there is a risk of depleting the parent stock of bees so much that chilled brood may result.

For the next week or so the new hive, or swarm stock, is the one which is likely to store surplus honey should weather and locality permit, as it has a concentration of foraging bees with virtually no brood to feed. The beekeeper, therefore, should ensure that adequate room is available in the supers. It is surprising how much such a stock can store during a short spell of favourable conditions *(Fig. 118)*.

The choice between using frames of foundation or drawn comb in the brood chamber may be perplexing when installing swarm in a new hive. If a supply of drawn comb is not available, the beekeeper has no option, but it is interesting to examine the merits of each choice. If the swarm is installed immediately prior to or during a heavy nectar flow, foundation is superior, for bees, unable to store honey in it until such time as it is drawn out into comb, are forced to store in the supers, especially if these are furnished with drawn comb. The result is that the surplus honey is contained in the supers and not used to clog up space in the brood chamber reserved for breeding purposes. When foundation is used during adverse or mediocre weather conditions however, bees tend to propolise and nibble it, so that many such combs have to be removed and discarded. An intimate knowledge of locality and a gamble with the weather may influence the beekeeper's decision, but where doubt arises it is advisable to use drawn comb if available. Apart from the danger of having the brood chamber temporarily clogged with stores, a swarm settles down and the brood nest expands more rapidly when drawn comb is used.

Although a colony is divided artificially into a parent colony and a swarm by drifting the bees, it does not necessarily follow that the swarm always settles down once installed in its new home. Much depends on the state of advancement of the swarming preparations in the original colony before the operation was carried out.

Once queen cells have reached the point of sealing or beyond, creating an artificial swarm does not always appear to satisfy the swarming impulse and it sometimes happens that the artificial swarm absconds from its hive within a short time. The presence of brood tends to discourage this, hence the comb of sealed brood installed, but once the queen commences to lay, more queen cells may be reared and a swarm issue at a later date. To avoid this it is advisable to check the swarm stock a week or so after instalment and if any queen cells are seen, these are destroyed, whereupon the stock generally settles down to normal running. If the artificial swarm is made when the queen cells contain only eggs or young larvae, this secondary swarming is not so common, although it is advisable to check up as before.

The parent stock, now deprived of its queen and much of its foraging force, normally has enough food for several weeks left in the brood chamber. To avoid the possibility of losing cast swarms, all queen cells except one in this stock should be destroyed *(Fig. 117)*. The selected queen cell should be seen to be developing properly and in a position where it is not likely to be damaged by manipulation. An unsealed queen cell

41

Fig. 113. *Pagden: The Queen is placed with frame of sealed brood into new hive with drawn combs.*

Fig. 114. *The new hive with queen (swarm stock) is placed on site of original hive (parent stock). Queen excluder is placed in position.*

Fig. 115. *The supers from the parent stock are added to the new swarm stock.*

Fig. 116. *The parent stock is removed to a fresh site. Drifting bees return to new hive on old site, join up with queen to form artificial swarm.*

Fig. 117. *Queen cells are destroyed in parent stock. One is left, or a new queen can be introduced.*

Fig. 118. *The swarm stock is checked to ensure ample room for storing surplus honey.*

Fig. 119. *The parent stock is checked to ascertain if queen right.*

Fig. 120. *The young queen has been mated and is laying.*

is sometimes preferred for this purpose, as, although the date of hatching is delayed, it is possible to determine that a queen larva is indeed present. This knowledge would be absent with a sealed cell, unless it was opened with the risk of its destruction. The comb containing the selected cell should be marked in some way - a drawing pin serves the purpose well - and the stock examined after a week. Any queen larvae being reared from the eggs or young larvae left in the hive originally, should be destroyed.

The disadvantage of leaving a queen to emerge in the parent stock is the delay created before she would finally mate and commence to lay. The introduction of a mated queen allows uninterrupted brood rearing *(Figs. 119-120)*.

Although the swarm stock is the more powerful foraging force for a few weeks, it dwindles in strength as the older bees die off without the constant hatch of young bees to replace them. The parent stock, although temporarily depleted of flying bees, soon gathers impetus as young bees hatch from the brood left behind and as the new queen reapidly increases her egg laying. This should be borne in mind when stocks are to be used for later nectar flows.

Although the Pagden method works satisfactorily, it entails a little unnecessary work and may not always take the fullest advantage of an existing nectar flow.

Heddon

This is a refinement of the Pagden method. The artificial swarm with the queen and honey supers is established on the site of the original stock, but instead of removing the parent stock to an entirely new site, it is placed at one side of the swarm stock hive with its entrance facing away at right angles to the original entrance *(Fig. 121)*. After two days the parent hive is shifted to the other side of the swarm stock, again with its entrance outward and away from the swarm stock. After a further two days the parent stock is shifted to an entirely different part of the apiary *(Fig. 122)*. The object of these moves is twofold. It will be seen that bees are drifted into the swarm stock at each move. This further supplements the foraging force of the honey-gathering swarm stock and at the same time depletes the parent stock of bees so much that it is most unlikely to throw cast swarms. The labour involved in destroying queen cells is thus avoided.

Snelgrove

Both the previous artificial swarming methods can be practised with any type of hive, single-or double-walled, and it will be noted that extra equipment in the form of a spare hive is required for each stock treated. Beekeepers using single-walled hives can cut down on this extra expense using slightly different methods.

So far we have drifted bees from parent stock to swarm stock, from side to side, or on a horizontal plane, but it is also possible to achieve the same results drifting from top to bottom, or on a perpendicular plane. The original way of doing this was by the Snelgrove method.

When a colony in a single-walled hive is found to be making swarming preparations, the queen on a sealed comb of brood is placed in a brood chamber filled with frames of foundation or drawncomb and the new brood chamber placed on the original floor of the hive. The queen excluder and supers are then added in the same way as in the Pagden method, but instead of moving the parent stock away, or to one side, it is placed over a Snelgrove board on top of the swarm stock. By a system of entrances which can be opened or shut and in close proximity, bees can be drifted from the top stock to the bottom one. The Snelgrove system works extremely well and can be used to advantage before colonies show signs of swarming preparations, but the method involves frequent visits to the hive to adjust the entrances and some think it a little complicated to perform.

A method becoming increasingly popular is, rightly or wrongly, termed the "modified Snelgrove method" and can be per-

formed using standard equipment. The Smith hive with its top bee space lends itself particularly well to such a manipulation.

It is possible to simulate this method in a double-walled hive by the use of a Shepherd tube - a device to "pipe" bees from the top brood chamber to a convenient exit.

The stock being treated is reassembled as before, that is, floor board; brood chamber with empty combs; along with a comb of sealed brood and queen; queen excluder; supers; board; brood chamber or chambers containing parent stock. Instead of using a Snelgrove board, the crown or cover board from the hive can easily be adapted by cutting a two-inch length out of its rim at an angle and pivoting the cut portion at one end by a pin so that a doorway is formed. The feed hole, if present, is completely closed so that there is no possibility of bees making contact through it; a piece of glass or plywood serves the purpose *(Figs. 125-128)*.

Flying bees returning to the original entrance join up with the queen and bees in the supers to form the artificial swarm stock. Bees from the parent stock also drift to the original entrance and thus the parent stock loses much of its strength. All queen cells are destroyed except one, unless a queen is available for introduction to the parent stock. As with the Heddon method the entrance to the parent stock can be manipulated to further drift bees to the swarm stock. This is achieved simply by turning the parent stock and its temporary floor board, after a lapse of a few days, so that its entrance faces the back. The principle of further drifting bees from the parent stock to the swarm stock is again followed so that the swarm stock is boosted in its foraging strength and the parent stock depleted to such an extent that the destruction of queen cells is not necessary.

After a young queen has hatched and mated from the parent stock and it is not intended to increase, the old queen is removed and the two stocks united. If the artificial swarm is made early in the season the united hive, having the laying power of two queens over a period and now headed by a young queen, is immensely powerful and is in ideal condition to take advantage of later summer flows. Should increase be desired it is a simple operaton to remove the parent stock, place it on a new floor board and assemble the hive.

It is necessary to check the swarm stock for queen cells during the first few weeks. If secondary swarming preparations are evident, destruction of the queen cells generally restrains further attempts.

The screen board used in transit makes a suitable temporary cover board for the parent colony, thus the only extra equipment required is a spare brood chamber with frames of foundation or drawn comb.

There are two drawbacks to this method. Bees from the top stock fly at shoulder level and can thus be a source of irritation and more labour is needed in removing the top stock and supers before the bottom stock can be examined.

When swarming preparations are seen to be imminent in a double-brood chamber hive and no spare brood chamber is available, reorganisation of the stock may control the situation. The combs present in the hive are grouped in the two brood chambers so that one has the sealed brood with the-queen and any empty combs and the other has the unsealed brood. (All queen cells are destroyed). The hive is then reassembled thus: floor board; brood chamber containing sealed brood, empty comb and queen; queen excluder; supers; cover board with top entrance; brood chamber containing remainder of brood; screen and roof. To avoid the risk of chilled brood in the upper chamber the feed hole in the cover board should be left open for a day. This allows young bees to reorganise themselves throughout the hive. Thereafter the top chamber should be completely cut off from the rest of the stock. It is necessary to follow the procedure afterwards as if for the ordinary "modified Snelgrove methods."

Fig. 121. *Heddon. Manipulated as for Pagden method but instead of removing parent stock to fresh site, it is placed at right angles to swarm stock.*

Fig. 122. *Heddon. After two days, the parent is shifted to other side of swarm stock. After a further two days, parent is removed to new site.*

Fig. 123. *A powerful stock is prepared for examination.*

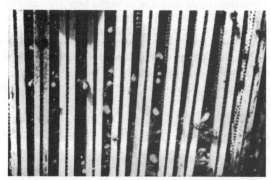

Fig. 124. *Queen cells are seen on splitting the brood chambers.*

Fig. 125. *Queen on comb of sealed brood is inserted into new chamber with drawn combs.*

Fig. 126. *The new chamber with queen is placed on original floorboard. Queen-excluder, supers and crown board are added.*

Fig. 127. *Detail of crown board showing cut rim which provides top entrance.*

Fig. 128. *Reassembled hive consists of—floor board brood chamber with queen, queen excluder, supers, crown board, original brood chambers, screen and roof.*

Shaken Swarm

For a beekeeper who has apiaries situated a few miles apart, the shaken swarm is a very satisfactory and easy method. Suitable travelling boxes with adequate ventilation are required, the wire screen boxes used for importing package bees being ideal.

The colony is subdued and the queen, when found, is placed in a matchbox. The combs in the brood chamber are lifted individually and shaken over the travelling box, so that the majority of the dislodged bees fall into it. Discretion must be used in the amount of bees removed from the colony, as there is a risk of the remaining brood being chilled through lack of bees.

The shaken bees form an irregular cluster in the box and the operator must work quickly otherwise they may fly back to the hive. The lid is secured and the box removed a short distance from the hive site, where bees adhering to the outside can be brushed off with a feather or handful of long grass. The queen is then run in through a small entrance made for the purpose and the shaken swarm is transported to another apiary where it can be hived.

Alternatively, combs can be shaken into the travelling box as before without finding the queen on the off-chance that she will be shaken in also. If the queen is missed, the stock is now so depleted of bees that it is unlikely to swarm. Even if it does, only a comparatively small number of bees will be lost. The hive from which a shaken swarm was taken should be treated as a parent stock, all queen cells except one being destroyed.

Demaree

As the swarming impulse can often be attributed to congestion in the brood nest, a system which would give a queen new ground to cover before swarming conditions arise would be an advantage. Such a system is found in the Demaree method.

The queen on a comb of brood is removed from the hive and placed in a spare brood chamber filled with empty combs and the hive reassembled thus: floor board; chamber containing queen; comb of brood and empty combs; queen excluder; original brood chamber or chambers; cover board; roof. Thus the colony is given a new area for brood rearing which is established in the bottom chamber, while the original brood, formerly utilising valuable laying space, is allowed to develop in the top chamber. The bees in the top brood chamber have access throughout the hive, but are nevertheless isolated from the influence of the queen. Queen cells frequently built as a result of this must be carefully searched for and destroyed, otherwise swarming may result. As there is no laying in the top chamber, one examination only is required after seven days of the operation. If supers are in use, these can be inserted on top of the queen excluder between the top and bottom brood chambers.

A stock so treated, generally settles down for the rest of the season without further trouble from swarming.

A useful variation of the Demaree method is the reversal of the order of the brood chambers. Thus: floor board; brood chamber containing original brood; supers; queen excluder; brood chamber with empty combs, comb of brood and queen; cover board; roof. More labour is involved in stripping down the hive for queen cell examination in the bottom chamber, but the advantage of this variation is seen when it is desired to empty old combs of brood and stores before discarding them. Once the brood has hatched out, bees are inclined to remove the stores from the bottom area and thus the combs are abandoned.

45

CHAPTER XI.

QUEEN REARING

In all branches of apiculture there is perhaps none so interesting or rewarding as the selection and rearing of queen bees to breed a strain which the beekeeper calculates to be most satisfactory and the extra time and labour entailed can pay handsome dividends.

It all too often happens that, because of the ease in procuring queens, increase is made from the first few stocks showing signs of swarming. Such management tends to propagate a strain of bee with swarming tendencies, to the possible exclusion of more valuable characteristics which may be found in other stocks in the same apiary. In summer management, an excessive-swarming strain of bee can be a liability, whereas characteristics such as resistance to disease, ease of handling, good capping if section honey is to be produced, foraging capabilities and stability on the combs when handling, are all desirable. These characteristics are not always present in a swarming stock and it would be regrettable to lose them simply through lack of a little extra labour and foresight. As in all animal husbandry, stock should be bred from the best strains available.

Queen Rearing Impulses

Queens are reared under three different impulses. These are swarming, supersedure and emergency. Swarm cells are generally composed of new wax at a time of year when swarming is prevalent, that is, from May to August, and may vary in number from three or four to twenty or over *(Fig. 129)*.

Supersedure cells are generally well-formed, inclined to be a trifle larger than swarm cells, occur at any time of year when brood is present, but appear more noticeable in spring or autumn. Only one to four are normally constructed *(Fig. 131)*.

Emergency cells are built if a queen is removed from a colony when brood is present. As no previous preparations have been made in the form of queen cell cups, the colony utilises eggs or larvae in selected worker cells. These are enlarged and the inmates treated in exactly the same way as if they were in normal queen cells. The appearance of an emergency cell is quite distinctive, as it started off as a worker cell on a horizontal plane before being drawn downwards and enlarged perpendicularly, resulting in a hook-shaped cell. These cells are generally quite numerous, varying from one or two to over twenty *(Fig. 130)*.

Queen Substance

At this point it would be interesting to examine the broad principles arising from the discovery of queen substance by Dr. C. G. Butler. That such a substance is present can be demonstrated by removing a mated queen from a colony and placing her in a matchbox. When a queen has been removed thus, many bees clamber over the face of the hive, obviously disturbed and as if searching for something *(Fig. 132)*. If the queen is transferred to another box and the original placed near the entrance to the hive, great interest is shown in it by the searching bees. If a similar box having no contact with a queen is placed near the entrance, little interest is shown in it. This proves that some influence had been left on the original box *(Fig. 133)*. If this colony was left queenless, within a short time many emergency queen cells would be built - the result of depriving the colony of a laying queen, or rather the substance which emanates from a laying queen.

A queen unable to lay fully because of damage or old age, only produces a limited amount of queen substance. As the colony is not completely deprived of the substance, the reaction is slower and a few queen cells only are built under the supersedure impulse.

When a queen's laying is restricted due to congestion in the brood nest, she does not emit a satisfactory amount of queen substance. In this case, queen cells may be constructed under the swarming impulse.

Inducing Swarm Cells

Procuring queens from either naturally or artificially swarmed colonies has already been mentioned when dealing with swarming colonies, but it is possible to induce this impulse by reversing normal methods of management.

A selected stock is built up on a double brood chamber. After separating sealed and unsealed brood combs, the queen is confined, by means of a queen excluder, in that part containing the unsealed brood. This is apt to result in swarming preparations, especially if storage room in the supers is also restricted and the queen cells formed can be utilised for re-queening other colonies. Unfortunately, if a non-swarming strain is chosen for this method, it cannot always be relied upon to produce an appreciable amount of queen cells.

Inducing Supersedure Cells

True supersedure often occurs at a time when mating conditions are unreliable and although it is possible to rear a few queens from a stock building cells under this impulse, there is a risk of rendering the colony queenless by the removal of such cells. However, this impulse can be created artificially by manipulation.

A stock is built up on a double brood chamber and queen excluder and supers added in the normal way. When conditions appear favourable, both in weather and strength of colony, the hive is reassembled thus: the queen is confined to the bottom brood chamber by means of the excluder, over which the supers are directly place, the top brood chamber being added on top of the supers. The hive now consists of: floor board; brood chamber containing brood and queen; queen excluder; supers; brood chamber containing brood, including eggs or young larvae; cover board; roof *(Fig. 141)*.

The stock is not rendered queenless and all worker bees have access throughout the hive. The bees in the top chamber, however, although having access to the queen, are nevertheless somewhat isolated from her influence and often set about rearing queen cells. These, of necessity, have the appearance of emergency cells, but are built under supersedure impulse, as the queen is still present in the hive. It is advisable to remove these queen cells before sealing stage to avoid any risk of swarming.

There are many arguments presented about the merits or otherwise under which impulse queens are best reared, but providing careful attention is given to the basic conditions required, all are equally satisfactory for practical purposes. Swarming and supersedure impulses are more variable and, therefore, not so readily controlled and by far the most reliable results come from the many methods based on the emergency impulse.

Making Nuclei

The simplest and most commonly used method of small-scale queen rearing is by creating nucleus hives and with a little experience in the management of these queen-rearing stocks, the principles of queen-rearing and increasing can be learned.

There are three factors to consider in making up a nucleus. They are food; the means by which the bees can rear a queen; and the supplying of the bees themselves.

Give Suitable Food

Combs of stores transferred from established colonies provide ideal food, a most useful form of comb for this purpose being a pollen-clogged comb often found at the extremity of a brood nest. Supplying of this pollen is important, particularly if queens are to be raised in the nucleus. It is preferable to give combs of stores rather than feeding, especially where established stocks are in the same apiary, as the danger of robbing is reduced and the sealed stores provide a form of food superior to sugar syrup *(Fig. 137)*.

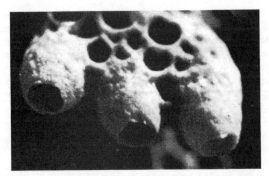

Fig. 129. Queen cells. Swarm cell cups. Constructed of new wax, number from three to over twenty.

Fig. 130. Queen cells. Emergency. Protrude from midrib of comb, have hook nose appearance.

Fig. 131. Queen cell. Supersedure. Well formed. Only one or two constructed at any one time. (Photo. M. Logan).

Fig. 132. Excited bees looking for queen after her removal from colony.

Fig. 133. "Queen substance." Matchbox on left had no queen. Box on right had contained a mated queen for five minutes.

Fig. 134. Introducing "ripe" queen cell to nucleus so that it is suspended between two combs.

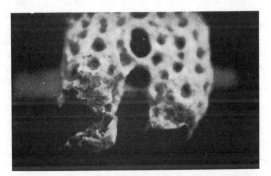

Fig. 135. Queen cells which have hatched. Flap is still adhering to one while other has open tip.

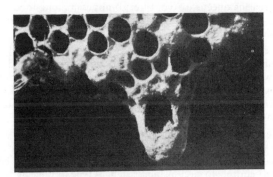

Fig. 136. Queen cell destroyed by bees. Side wall has been torn down.

Providing a Queen

A queen or queen cell can be introduced to a nucleus, but where the nucleus has to rear its own queen, fertile eggs or larvae of a suitable age must be inserted. Eggs are generally preferable, because to the inexperienced, the choice of larvae under 36-hours old may present difficulty. Moreover, if larvae just under 36-hours old are selected, the newly-formed nucleus might not reach its peak of queenlessness until several hours have elapsed and the consequent delayed feeding of such larvae may result in an inferior queen.

A comb containing hatching brood with a small area of eggs around the centre should be selected *(Figs. 6 and 138)*.

More Bees!

A common fault when forming a nucleus is that of shortage of bees, especially when the nucleus is made up in the same apiary as the parent stock, for the majority of flying bees will invariably drift back to the parent hive. It is not sufficient simply to remove combs covered with bees and place them in a nucleus box, as frequently later examination will reveal the activities of robber bees, and inside, a few bees huddled together on a patch of chilled brood. Loose grass forced into the entrance of a nucleus does prevent a slight amount of drifting, but cannot be relied upon entirely.

During the active season when a comb is removed from the brood nest and given a sharp shake, the majority of bees are dislodged. Those remaining on the comb are mainly young bees, easily detected by their soft, downy appearance and greyish colour *(Fig. 6)*. These young bees will not drift back to the parent stock, because when they do fly from the nucleus, they will orientate themselves from it and return to it. They also have their brood food glands developing and where queen rearing is to be carried out, this is of paramount importance. Young bees having their full adult life ahead are better equipped to maintain the colony until the queen mates and her brood hatches out to manage the new colony.

To ensure adequate stocking of bees, therefore, remove the queen, go through the parent colony, then by shaking, dislodge the older bees from the combs and shake the remaining young bees into the nucleus box. As a general guide, it is advisable to shake in three or four combs of young bees for every comb of brood *(Fig. 139)*.

Types of Nuclei

These three factors form the structure on which nuclei are made, but the size of the nucleus depends upon requirements. For rearing queens, two or three combs containing food and eggs or larvae and an abundance of young bees is generally sufficient.

A very small nucleus is adequate for queen mating. Two combs, one containing food, the other hatching brood or drawn comb, can be chosen for convenience and to a nucleus such as this, a ripe queen cell or a virgin queen is introduced. Queens generally mate more quickly from such a small unit than from an established colony.

Where nuclei are made with the intention of forming new colonies in time to build up for later honey flows, a larger amount of combs and bees is desirable. The number of combs can be left entirely to circumstances such as type of nucleus box, the extent to which the beekeeper wishes to deplete the parent colony, and number of drawn combs available.

As a swarm control measure, nuclei can be taken from stocks showing signs of swarming and formed either with the old queen or simply by depriving the colony of some brood and bees.

The Housing Problem

Three types of accommodation are in use for nuclei. An empty hive, which, if available, is very suitable, any excess room being shut off by dummy boards, and the entrance reduced to cut down the risk of robbing. Nuclei boxes of various designs

and shapes are much in evidence, but although having the advantage of mobility as a unit, they have several drawbacks. When not in use they require almost as much attention as a hive. Nuclei boxes are quite expensive and involve as much work in construction as a hive.

Beekeepers using single-walled hives can utilise a standard brood chamber which can remain as an ordinary hive component when the occasion arises, or can be divided into compartments to house several nuclei. The brood chamber is divided by means of division boards into three or four compartments, but it is essential that these, together with the floor board or adapted cover board, should be close-fitting. The latter are divided by wooden strips and 1 inch x ⅜ inch entrances provided for each compartment so that they face in different directions. Sawcuts made in the brood chamber sides with sheets of aluminium or other metal cut to a size that allows them to slide into place, ensure properly sealed compartments *(Fig. 140)*. This is important, for if bees have contact, it may be found that queens mysteriously disappear.

A chamber divided into four compartments offers maximum use of available space for queen mating, but the combs are not easily manipulated. A more useful box is divided into three compartments by two division boards, giving ample room to manipulate. A brood chamber nuclei box can be set on top of an established hive, with consequent saving of equipment, and contrary to what one might expect from the proximity of the entrances, queen matings are quite successful.

Miller Method

When a beekeeper does not wish to interfere unduly with his best stock, but nevertheless would like to rear queens from it, or if a selected stock appears loath to raise many queen cells, the most satisfactory method of queen rearing is utilising another stock of bees. For identification, the stock from which it is desired to rear queens is termed the "breeder" and that which will carry out the rearing, the "rearing" stock.

The rearing stock must be strong and have an ample amount of young bees of brood-food-secreting age. A colony making swarming preparation is ideal for the purpose.

A comb is prepared beforehand by inserting a frame containing diagonally-cut foundation into any strong stock *(Fig. 142)* until it is partly drawn and removed before it is filled with brood or stores. This prepared comb is inserted into the centre of the breeder stock brood nest. If a nectar flow is not present, feeding with thin syrup will induce continued brood rearing so that four days after insertion, the prepared comb will be laid up with eggs or newly-hatched larvae. The queen and any combs containing eggs or young larvae are removed from the rearing stock and can be conveniently housed in a newly-made-up nucleus, then the prepared comb from the breeder, containing eggs, is transferred to the centre of the brood nest in the rearing stock. As the rearing stock is deprived of its own eggs and young larvae, it is forced to rear queen cells from the eggs or larvae supplied from the breeder, thus queens from a selected strain are obtained under ideal conditions and with the minimum of disturbance to the breeder stock.

It will be found that many of the queen cell so formed are built at the perimeter of the comb in the prepared frame and that sometimes two or more are attached, making separation without destroying one or both in the process very difficult. To avoid this, some eggs on the perimeter should be destroyed by depressing them with a match, a good pattern resulting from destroying two, leaving one, destroying two and so on, before the comb is placed in the rearing stock *(Figs. 143 and 144)*. Depending on the ages of the eggs or larvae originally inserted, careful calculations will indicate when the queen cells are due to hatch and these must be removed from the rearing stock beforehand, otherwise the first queen emerging may destroy the remainder, or the colony may throw a swarm. Ripe queen cells are carefully cut from the comb with a penknife leaving substantial "heels" by which they can be handled.

Fig. 137. *Nucleus-making comb of honey and pollen stores.*

Fig. 138. *Comb of hatching brood with eggs or young larvae in centre.*

Fig. 139. *Shaking young bees into nucleus. Queen has been removed previously.*

Fig. 140. *A convenient type of divided nucleus box.*

Fig. 141. *Splitting a double brood chamber with a honey super encourages the rearing of queen cells.*

Fig. 142. *Prepared frame of foundation inserted into "breeder" stock.*

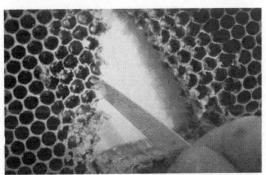

Fig. 143. *The scalloped comb from "breeder" is laid up with eggs. Every second and third egg is destroyed along perimeter of comb.*

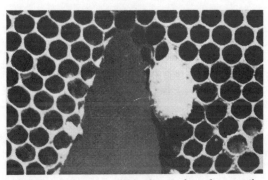

Fig. 144. *The queen cells develop singly and are easily removed*

They are then introduced individually to queenless colonies or nuclei for hatching and subsequent mating. Care must be taken to avoid rough handling or chilling.

There are many other satisfactory methods of queen rearing but all are based on the same principle, namely, providing a strong, queenless colony with eggs or larvae from a selected breeder colony. Among these may be mentioned the Alley, Doolittle and Stanley systems, which are adopted by the bigger beekeeper who sometimes specialises in queen rearing.

When introducing a ripe queen cell into a nucleus or stock, one method is to make a depression on the face of the comb with the thumb and affix the queen cell in place by its severed "heel" or comb. Care must be taken to ensure the tip of the cell is free, allowing bees to thin down the wax sealing and eventually permitting the queen to emerge. A satisfactory alternative is simply to dangle the queen cell by its heel between two frames, which may have to be prised apart slightly *(Fig. 134)*. An advantage of this method is that much information can be gained later without handling combs in any way.

When a queen hatches she cuts a circular flap from the tip of her cell, leaving a round orifice which is readily seen for some days or weeks *(Fig. 135)* until worker bees eventually cut back the empty cell close to its base. Sometimes the flap is sealed back in place after the queen has emerged. It is not uncommon to find a worker bee entombed in such a queen cell, which she has entered probably with the intention of cleaning it out. All these signs point to the fact that a queen bee has indeed hatched from a cell.

When an unhatched queen is destroyed by another queen, or by worker bees, the cell is attacked from the side and the dead body removed via this breach *(Fig. 136)*. This indicates either that another queen is present or that the colony has not accepted the queen cell for some other reason.

It is not within the province of the majority of beekeepers in this country to carry out the controlled mating of queen bees, largely because of the proximity of other apiaries. True, such control can be performed by instrumental insemination, but few beekeepers can undertake this. There are isolated areas where queens can be mated with drones from selected hives but these are few and far between and again only in reach of a favoured minority.

A reasonable measure of success, however, can be obtained by flooding an apiary with selected drones in the hope that they will mate with any queen flying from the same apiary. To this end, drone rearing is encouraged in the selected stocks and eliminated as far as possible in those thought to have undesirable qualities. Drone base foundation is available and can be used to advantage in rearing drones where desired.

A proportion of poor mating results in some apiary sites during the past, may be attributed to their distance from drone assembly areas. It is perhaps significant that introduced, exotic races and crosses of honey bees to a district, are gradually replaced without human interference by native-type bees within a few years.

Although it is true that a strain of bee is influenced by the drone which mates with the queen, much can be done by the beekeeper in the careful selection of stock from which his queens are reared.

CHAPTER XII

UNITING AND QUEEN INTRODUCTION.

Every colony of bees has its own particular colony odour derived from the countless combinations of food sources available and it is through this medium that bees are able to recognise and if necessary repel strangers. In introducing bees to a colony, this must be taken into account otherwise a belligerent situation may arise with the loss of many bees.

Occasions arise when it is advantageous to combine or unite colonies, for example, when one is queenless or when two or more have insufficient bees independently, to form a honey-gathering stock.

During a heavy nectar flow it is likely that colonies in the same apiary would be gathering from the same source and at such times uniting is a simple operation. After subduing, shake the bees off the combs from one stock on to the floor of its hive, withholding a few shaken combs from the chamber. Remove the unwanted queen in the second stock and shake the bees from it among those on the floor of the first hive. Combs of brood are arranged into a single or double brood chamber, depending on numbers *(Fig. 145)*. The subduing and shaking so demoralises the colonies that union takes place quite peacefully, but it must be emphasised that this should only be carried out during a good nectar flow, otherwise pandemonium may break loose. Similar conditions can be created artificially when no flow is present by spraying the bees with peppermint water, or dusting with flour. This masks colony odour, but this latter operation is tedious and more risky. As an added precaution, some prefer to cage the queen for some time in the united stocks.

Newspaper Method

At times of the year when fresh nectar is unavailable, the orthodox newspaper method should be employed; indeed, this method can be used at any time when the beekeeper is in doubt. The unwanted queen is removed from one colony and a single sheet of newspaper is placed over the top of the chamber, completely covering it. If it is windy, a few drawing pins will tack the paper in position. The newspaper is perforated with small holes with a penknife, wire nail, or corner of a hive tool, but not so as to allow bees direct access *(Fig. 146)*. The stock containing the selected queen is now lifted in its brood chamber off the floorboard of its hive and placed directly over the newspaper, a closed cover board or screen board being used on top to render it bee-proof *(Fig. 147)*. The colony odours are able to mingle without bees having direct contact with each other, so that by the time the paper is gnawed away the bees have acquired a common colony odour and unite without further trouble. Not only do the odours merge, but bees are able to participate in food exchange via their mouthparts through the perforations and in so doing, gradually acquire the same odour.

Queen Introduction

As has been described, bees sometimes commit reginacide by "balling" the queen and in queen introduction, the colony odour from a strange queen may stimulate such behaviour. When introducing queen bees, therefore, some means of isolating her from possible harm should be devised. At the same time, the mingling of odour, or, even better, the receiving of food, renders her more acceptable. The functions of the numerous queen introducton cages on the market are all based on these assertions.

To illustrate the principles involved let us examine what takes place when a queen is introduced using the "Chantry" queen introduction cage *(Fig. 148)*. This apparatus consists of a harp-shaped piece of wood, having a cavity at its broadest part,

which is covered on one side by wire gauze. When the open side is fixed to a brood comb, a cage is formed in which the queen is imprisoned. Two tunnels lead from the cavity. One is short and covered at the cavity end with a piece of queen excluder, the other is longer and has no obstruction. Both tunnels are filled with a stiff dough made from icing sugar and honey which bees from the colony commence eating a way through. Naturally, bees excavate the shorter tunnel first and are able to enter the cavity containing the queen one at a time. Because of the queen excluder she is still imprisoned and the situation arises where bees mingle with her, feed her with food from the colony and thus impart the colony odour. As bees attack a queen by balling, the few bees present are not a menace. Meantime, other bees eating a way through the longer tunnel eventually break through and the acclimatised queen is now able to escape and take up her duties in the colony.

Matchbox Method

Much the same results are obtained with far less trouble by the matchbox method. The queen is placed on her own in a cardboard-type matchbox (e.g. Bluebell, Punch, Pearl, etc.) which has been empty of matches for some time and the lid is closed to one-eighth of an inch (3 mm.). The box with queen is now placed on the floor of the hive, or rested on top of the brood chamber frames, care being taken in either case to ensure bees have ready access to the opening. The queen soon becomes hungry and solicits food, which is seldom refused and is fed to her via her mouth parts through the opening. This direct feeding has the effect of transmitting the colony odour to the queen very quickly. She in turn is apt to lose some of her agitation on receiving such attention. Meanwhile, bees are nibbling the matchbox opening and eventually a big enough hole is made for a worker to pass through, but still too small for a queen, thus a queen excluder is automatically created similar to that of the more complicated cage. Finally the hole is enlarged and the queen released. This method, because of its mere simplicity, is apt to be overlooked, or even scorned in favour of the more impressive looking cages available but often it is more reliable than most queen introduction cages *(Fig. 149)*.

Whyte Cage

A very satisfactory method of introduction is by the use of the Whyte introduction cage. A comb of hatching brood is shaken free of bees and placed, with the queen, in the cage, which in turn is placed in the hive brood chamber. The young bees emerging from the cells are not likely to damage the queen indeed they tend her and are able to attend to the young larvae when they hatch from the new queen's eggs. The mere fact of the queen establishing a brood nest in the colony ensures her stay without antagonism. After a week or ten days the queen and her comb of brood are removed from the cage and replaced in the brood chamber.

Although this method is most reliable and can function where other methods fail, such as when introducing a queen into a colony which has been queenless for a long period, it will be seen that a considerable amount of time and labour is entailed which many consider to be unjustified.

Postal Cage

The postal cage consisting of a block of wood with three cavities joined by short passages, one of which is filled with candy, should be regarded with suspicion. The general mode of use is simply to tear off the paper covering the outside entrance to the candy-filled cavity and allow bees from the colony to eat their way through, as with the Chantry cage. Unfortunately the attendant bees in the cage are often killed when union takes place and there is a risk of the queen being killed

51

Fig. 145. *Uniting. Shaking alternate combs of bees from two stocks into one hive can be carried out during a nectar flow.*

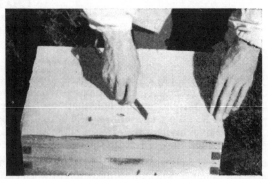

Fig. 146. *Uniting. Newspaper is pierced with corner of hive tool.*

Fig. 147. *Uniting. The two colonies will unite peaceably when paper barrier is chewed down.*

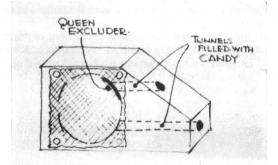

Fig. 148. *Diagram of "chantry" queen introduction cage.*

Fig. 149. *Matchbox used to introduce queen.*

Fig. 150. *Piece of comb containing eggs or young larvae is placed over frames where queenlessness is in doubt.*

Fig. 151. *Piece of comb showing normal brood indicating that a queen is present.*

Fig. 152. *Piece of comb showing developing queen cells denotes colony is indeed queenless.*

or maimed in the ensuing melee. If it is decided to use this method of introduction, it is better to open the gauze covering and release the attendant bees, leaving the queen on her own. Better still, transfer her to a matchbox, which is best carried out indoors or in a car, in case the queen takes flight, and proceed as described.

Preliminary Tests

Many of the disappointments in queen introduction can be traced not to the method, but to the actual state of the colony and the queen. For instance, unless the beekeeper has actually removed a queen from a stock, can he be sure that the colony is indeed queenless? It so often happens that when a beekeeper examines a stock he assumes it to be queenless simply because there is no evidence of brood. Very often a queen cell has been overlooked during a previous inspection and a virgin queen is very difficult to spot in a populous colony.

In cases of doubt there is one simple test, which can be applied during the active season. A comb containing eggs or young larvae is removed from another stock and placed in the centre of the suspected stock's brood chamber; alternatively, a piece of comb with eggs or young larvae is placed over the top of the brood chamber frames, face downwards *(Fig. 150).* Five days later the introduced cells are examined. If the brood is being reared as normal worker larvae there is almost sure to be a queen present, *(Fig. 151)* but if an attempt is made to draw emergency queen cells it can safely be assumed that the colony is indeed queenless and a queen can be introduced *(Fig. 152).*

When a stock has been queenless for a considerable period, say over eight weeks, it may be very difficult to introduce a queen satisfactorily and even if one is accepted, the lack of young bees to act as nurses is a serious hindrance to colony build-up. Such a stock is better united to a queen-right one either by methods described, or by drifting. This applies especially in a case where laying workers are present.

If a stock is known to be queenless it may be thought desirable to introduce a virgin queen. If a virgin is newly-emerged from her cell and before she acquired any distinct odour, it is possible to introduce her directly by running her in at the entrance, or placing her on a brood comb of the colony into which she is to be introduced. If she has spent a few hours in her original home, it may be very difficult to have her accepted in another colony. In this event it is better to allow her to mate and commence laying in the original colony before attempting introduction elsewhere.

CHAPTER XIII

LATE SUMMER MANAGEMENT

Colony Rhythm

Colonies situated in early localities may build up on such sources as fruit blossom, dandelion and sycamore and reach the peak of brood-rearing by mid-June. This results in the foraging force being at its maximum in July, ready to take full advantage of mid-summer flows such as clover, lime and bell heather. Thereafter these colonies are apt to curtail brood-rearing and the foraging force diminishes as old bees die off.

Colonies situated permanently in late localities such as heather areas, however, generally retard brood-rearing so that its peak is in July and the foraging strength is at its maximum to take advantage of these later flows. This applies to the majority of races and crosses of honey bees kept in this country and not to some strains of Italian bees, which are inclined to breed heavily throughout the season, sometimes to the detriment of the secured honey crop.

In an exceptional season, colonies which have taken full advantage of mid-summer flows and have been transported to the heather, may also gather a creditable surplus from this later source, but generally results are disappointing. Frequently these stocks are brought back with the honey supers neglected and such honey as has been gathered, stored in the brood chambers. The following spring many of these stocks emerge in a weakened condition, as the hatch of young bees at the heather had not been sufficient to compensate for the heavy death rate of the adult foragers.

Although it may be thought profitable to work stocks on only one group of flows, it is possible to utilise them for both mid-summer and late flows with the following management.

Preparing for the Heather

As ling heather may commence to secrete nectar in early seasons during the last week of July, let us follow the sequence of management to have a stock prepared for migration sometime around 21st July.

Spring and summer management in the form of swarm control and supering is carried out as already described, the colony being housed in a double brood chamber throughout this period. Some give three or more such brood chambers, although as with premature supering, there is a tendency for the colony to "chimney". The "chimneying" in this case is caused by the colony's urge to expand in an upward direction rather than sideways, so that the brood nest is in the form of a tall, comparatively thin area *(Fig. 153)*. While this again in itself is not detrimental to the colony, much wastage of space results and the employment of more equipment is necessary. Whatever course is adopted, the principle is to provide the colony with ample accommodation for brood-rearing throughout the early summer.

Assuming the stock has shown no signs of swarm preparations, it is examined and dealt with on some suitable day at the end of June *(Fig. 154)*. The colony is subdued; roof, supers and queen excluder are removed in the usual manner, then the combs in the top brood chamber are taken one by one and the bees shaken off into the bottom brood chamber *(Fig. 155)*. This saves time in searching for the queen, for if she is present in the top brood chamber she is shaken down with the rest of the bees. The hive is then reassembled thus: floorboard; brood chamber with queen; queen excluder; brood chamber; supers; cover; roof *(Figs. 156 and 158)*.

Drone brood can be destroyed in the top chamber by mashing it with the hive tool and this not only prevents the trapping of hatched drones above the queen excluder, but also reduces the time between operations by three days *(Fig. 157)*.

All brood in the top brood chamber will have hatched after 24 days ((21 days if drone brood has been destroyed) and if a nectar flow had persisted in the interim, the vacated cells would probably be filled with honey. The top brood chamber is now virtually a honey super and the colony has been restricted to a single brood chamber.

A few days before transporting, the combs in the top chamber are again shaken free of bees and either added to another stock or placed in a suitable store *(Fig. 159)*. The heather-going stock now consists of a very compact, single brood chamber over which is placed a queen excluder and the supers to be used for the heather flow. The original honey supers from this stock are removed either at the first operation or up to any time before the final re-arrangement. Combs containing sealed and ripe honey should be extracted immediately, while those with unripe honey are added to another stock for finishing off.

When the stock is returned from the heather, all honey produced above the queen excluder is removed as surplus, along with the queen excluder, then the original top brood chamber, which, in most seasons, should be well-filled with stores, is returned to its position on the hive. The stock once again consists of a double brood chamber and if the bulk of the stores is positioned above the brood nest, ideal conditions for wintering result. It may be advisable to feed some stocks in the autumn for the purpose of filling intervening areas of empty cells in the top chamber combs to ensure an unbroken canopy of stores above the winter cluster.

There are many variations and refinements of these preparations. Some, for instance, carry out a modification of the Demaree method by confining the queen, using a queen excluder, along with sealed brood and empty combs in the bottom chamber. The sealed brood hatches and creates room for the queen to lay, while the unsealed brood develops and the vacated cells are filled with stores as before. There is a saving of time by confining the queen in the bottom chamber along with unsealed brood so that the sealed brood is left in the top chamber, but there is a greater risk of swarming. It is also possible in some cases to reduce the stock to a single brood chamber by removing combs without brood or by distributing surplus combs of brood to other stocks.

Re-queening

A young queen of the current season mated between May and July does not reach her peak of laying until later in the season and normally continues laying after older queens have ceased. If such a queen is introduced to a colony which has already reached its maximum in brood-rearing a secondary peak of brood-rearing is often achieved. In many cases this does not greatly affect the foraging force in time for later flows, but the amount of brood laid by the young queen prevents the storing of honey in the brood-chamber, and forces bees to utilise the honey supers. What is most important, however, is the rearing of young bees to carry through winter and this reflects on the development of the colony the following year.

A current year's queen can be introduced to a heather-going stock at the first re-arranging of the hive, or at any time prior to moving, after removing the old queen *Fig. 160)*. Parent stocks from naturally or artificially swarmed stocks are ideal for heather work, especially if they were formed early in the season and it is possible to boost such stocks by drifting or uniting other stocks to them. It is most unusual for a colony headed by a current year's queen to develop swarming tendencies during that year.

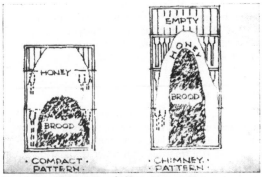

Fig. 153. *Illustration of chimneying.*

Fig. 154. *Double brood chamber hive with supers requires reducing before move to heather.*

Fig. 155. *Supers are removed. All bees including queen are shaken from top brood chamber into bottom brood chamber.*

Fig. 156. *Top brood chamber is removed. Queen excluder is placed on bottom brood chamber.*

Fig. 157. *Drone brood is destroyed in top chamber to prevent drones blocking queen excluder.*

Fig. 158. *Hive is reassembled. Supers may be removed at this stage.*

Fig 159. *After 3 weeks bees are shaken and brushed from broodless top chamber which is stored to await return from heather.*

Fig. 160. *Introducing mated queen of the current season ensures young bees to compensate for heavy death rate at heather.*

Supering for Heather

Because of the peculiar characteristics of ling heather honey, supering often differs from that of other honeycrops to avoid the wastage of drawn honey comb. Section honey can be produced and at this time of year, warm packing used to conserve the heat necessary for wax secretion.

Stocks which have been working on clover immediately before migration to heather are apt to continue working on this former source should it be available at the heather site to the exclusion of the heather itself, even although it may be secreting freely. It is for this reason that many beekeepers do not move to the heather until a later date. The fluctuations in seasons, however, are so diverse that it is difficult to forecast on what date heather will commence yielding and good surplus crops are often lost through this delay.

Experiments have demonstrated that bees can be trained to work a certain crop by introducing the scent of that crop to the colony. Beekeepers have used this principle over many years before moving to the heather, by inserting "bait" sections. These are partially-filled heather honey sections retained from the previous year and two or three of them are introduced to the centre of each section crate. The partly drawn comb encourages bees to take quicker possession of the crates while the scent of the honey influences the foraging outside *(Fig. 166)*.

Sections can be fitted with either full sheets of foundation or "starters", of which there are a great variety. Starters are simply small pieces of foundation cut to different shapes, such as a triangle, oblong or thin strips, and inserted into the sections *(Fig. 161)*. Bees are able to cluster in crates of sections with starters and take to them more readily than with full sheets. The completed honey comb is thought to be superior, as the midrib is a virgin comb, which is more pleasing to the palate than foundation. The disadvantages of starters are that the combs are sometimes not evenly drawn and the finished sections may not be of standard weight.

The split, three-way section is more quickly assembled than the split and grooved section, as one sheet foundation can be readily inserted into three sections at a time after they have been positioned in the crate *(Fig. 162)*.

The circular, plastic "Cobana" section is superior in many ways to the square wooden section, although the initial cost of the equipment is rather heavy *(Figs. 163-165)*. Because of the round area, comb is drawn to the outside rings, unlike the square sections, whose corners are often left neglected. Unlike wooden sections, there is virtually no waste of material through stale foundation, as this can be easily removed and replaced where necessary and the cleaning and packing of the finished article is speedily accomplished. The old pattern of National and Smith hive section crates make ideal holders for the "Cobana" section racks.

Shallow frames of foundation or drawn combs are used for heather by many in the same way as for other honey crops, the honey being removed by various processes, such as cutting out and pressing, scraping and pressing, or by loosening and extracting.

Cut Comb Honey

The production of cut comb or package honey is increasing in popularity and is now sometimes used for other honeys, apart from ling heather. Cut comb honey can be produced in ordinary frames using thin super foundation in either full sheet or starter form, or in a hive part known as a "cog", "eke" or "cap". The "cog" consists of a suitably-sized box without top or bottom on which are affixed slats of wood which support the starters and the combs when drawn. The dimensions of the "cog" and spacing of the combs can vary, but convenient measurements are 4½ inches (108 mm.) deep, which allows two such cogs to fit snugly in a deep chamber, and the starter foundation spaced at 1½ inch (38 mm.) intervals. These foundation starters can be compressed between two narrow wooden slats, or "soldered" on to one broader slat with melted beeswax and the slats are held in position by frame nails driven through the sides of the cog and left protruding ⅛inch (3 mm.) or so to allow easy withdrawal *(Fig. 167)*.

When a cog is placed over a queen excluder or another cog or super, the combs built from it are likely to be attached at their base to whatever is below. It is necessary in such cases to cut the comb at its juncture and this can be done by first prising up the "cog" slightly with a hive tool then inserting a cheese wire which is then drawn through the space created. If small pieces of wood section or matchsticks are inserted at the corners, bees will clear up the honey escaping from the severed cells within a few hours, but, unfortunately a few combs often fracture during the separating operation and the operator is left with a very awkward crop to handle.

The use of plastic sheeting simplifies the production of cut comb honey in "cogs", horticultural grade polythene proving ideal for the purpose. A sheet of this material is cut to a size to leave a clear space of 1 inch (25 mm.) all round the inside of the cog and is fixed to the centre of the brood chamber frame tops with drawing pins. This allows ample space for the passage of bees but offers a barrier, or rather a deterrent to the queen and the storage of pollen above is most unlikely.

Although this plastic sheet can be used as a form of queen excluder at any time of year, it is not reliable and some prefer to use it in conjunction with a normal excluder. Its main function for "cog" production is to keep the comb in each part of the hive separated. Bees dislike building wax on such plastic and are even loath to propolise it, hence a bee space is left above the sheet and the finished "cog" can be removed with the same ease as a completed, properly-spaced super without resorting to cutting *(Fig. 168)*. If a second or third "cog" has to be added to a stock it is, of course, necessary to insert a similar sheet between each joint. Polythene sheeting is also very satisfactory for covering crates of sections and little propolising occurs on the section tops. The sheet should be pulled tightly over the surface and secured with a few drawing pins.

Fig. 161. *Section showing starter: split and grooved section: three split-three-way sections using one sheet of foundation.*

Fig. 162. *Crate of three-way sections. Fitting foundation into filled crate saves much time.*

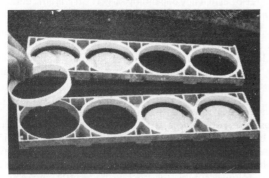

Fig. 163. *Plastic "cobana" section holder open, showing insertion of rings.*

Fig. 164. *Foundation being placed in "cobana" section holder.*

Fig. 165. *Closed "cobana" section holder fitted with rings and foundation. Parts of the plastic mould act as dividers.*

Fig. 166. *Introducing "bait" sections before moving to heather.*

Fig. 167. *"Eke" or "cog" showing foundation starters set inside Smith Super.*

Fig. 168. *Finished cog. (Photo. M. Braithwaite.)*

CHAPTER XIV.

DEALING WITH THE HONEY CROP.

Section honey should be removed from the hive as soon as is practicable to avoid its becoming travel-stained, but combs for extracting can be taken off at various times during summer, or left until the end of the season, when they can be removed in one operation. Travel-staining is a term used to describe the appearance of comb which has had contact with bees over a period and is thought to be caused by the deposit of propolis from their bodies. This can detract from the appearance of the pearly-white cappings of new section honey comb, but makes little difference to honey which is to be uncapped before extraction.

Honey should not normally be removed until it is ripe and sealed over, although there are seasons when colonies are unable to complete the sealing of ripe honey. The extraction of unripe or "green" honey introduces a higher water content than is desirable, with the resultant risk of fermentation. In cases of doubt, combs containing open cells of honey should be given a heavy shake to ascertain the degree of ripeness. If no honey is dislodged it is fit for extracting, but if some shakes out, the combs should be returned to the super, or where this is not practicable, segregated from the main crop.

Removing the Honey Crop

The use of the clearing board is the most popular method among small beekeepers for removing surplus honey from the hive, as it entails little handling of bees. Occasions arise, however, when the clearing board may prove a failure owing to carelessness or neglect by the beekeeper.

There are many types of "escapes", but in this country the Porter escape is almost exclusively used. This consists of a metal framework, so made that a T-shaped tunnel is formed, two entrances of which are fitted with pairs of fine springs. These springs are fixed so that the weight of a small body forces them open from the inside, but when they spring back, they form an effective barrier from the outside; thus bees are able to travel down the open tunnel and through either of the spring-loaded exits, but are unable to force their way back again. The Porter escape is a delicate piece of mechanism and frequently its failure can be attributed to rough or careless handling. The practice of using a dual-purpose escape and crown board throughout the year should be avoided unless the escape is placed in position only when required. The retention of the escape on the board throughout winter impedes through-ventilation and, if left during the active season, is liable to be covered with propolis, or have brace comb built in or around it, rendering it completely useless. It is essential that the spacing between the tips of the springs be properly adjusted, for if set too closely together, bees are unable to push their way past and, if too widely set apart, allows the escaping bees to return. It is difficult to set the springs correctly from the outside, but the Porter escape is so made that the top can slide off exposing the springs, which should be set approximately ⅛-inch (3 mm.) apart *(Fig. 169)*. It may be found that an escape is stiff to dismantle, but gentle prising with a blade will ease the flanges and allow this to be done. When obtaining a new Porter escape, it is advisable to open it and smear the sliding parts with vaseline, which prevents propolising and ensures subsequent ease of opening.

When a clearing board has been placed underneath an occupied super, some bees may panic and uncap honey cells, the cappings of which may drop on the escape and clog the passages. Where a queen excluder is not used, stray drones may be present and they also may cause an obstruction as they attempt to force an exit. Clearing boards having two or more escapes help to overcome this difficulty and have the advantage of clearing the supers more rapidly. This point should

be noted when section crates are being cleared, as there is less risk of having a few cells torn open by panicking or hungry bees.

The use of a strong carbolic cloth for driving bees out of honey supers should be avoided, especially by those producing sections, as the honey can absorb the taint of the acid. It is not infrequently at honey shows that such tainted sections have been rejected by judges. The chemicals, Propionic anhydride and benzaldehyde have been used with varying results, the degree of efficiency depending largely on climatic conditions. Unlike carbolic acid, they do not appear to taint the honey.

Beekeepers owning out-apiaries may find the shaking method to be advantageous, as the use of the clearing board entails a double journey and a lapse of 12-48 hours to allow the supers to be cleared. If a nectar flow is present, almost any manipulation can be carried out, including the removal of honey, but if the temperature is sufficiently high to allow bees to fly and a nectar dearth is present, combs of honey should not be exposed, as robber bees are attracted to each hive opened and robbing may spread through-out the apiary. It is possible to make quick manipulations during cold or wet weather, as then colonies tend to occupy only the brood chambers. The method is as follows: subdue the stock using as little smoke as possible, then remove the roof and crown board or covers. An empty super or section crate is set on the inverted roof beside the hive, then the combs of honey are quickly but carefully removed, each one being given a quick shake to remove the majority of bees; a large feather will dislodge any still adhering to the comb. The feather does not irritate bees so much as a bee brush and is more convenient for reaching crevices or pot-holes present in the comb *(Fig. 170)*. The cleared comb is now placed in the empty super and this process repeated until all the combs are cleared. Where more than one super of honey has to be cleared from one hive, it is advisable to remove all the supers first, setting them on the upturned roof of the hive. The bees are then shaken off as before and after the first super is cleared it will be found that an empty one is left, which in turn is used as a receptacle for the contents of the next super, and so on. If a nectar flow is present, this shaking method can be carried out in exactly the same manner. During warmer weather, however, there will be a larger quantity of bees in the supers and shaking them over the brood chamber is apt to cause many of them to fall over the sides. Young bees particularly may be lost through this. An empty super exchanged for the full ones will act as a funnel, so that combs can be shaken inside it.

There is a grave risk of robbing in removing supers or crates of honey and setting them uncovered some distance away, leaving the bees inside free to fly back to their own hive. Moreover, young bees, unable to fly, remain in he supers and have either to be carried back to the hive or left to perish with cold. All cleared combs, where taken off by shaking or left in position over a clearing board, cease to become part of the bee colony and are fair game to robber bees. Every care should be taken to make cleared honey safe from robber bees.

The use of high velocity air pressure such as is generated in "Hive Blowers" used extensively in America is an advancement proving invaluable in the hands of the large operator. With this method, the supers are simply lifted from the hive onto a framework and an air jet blows bees from between the combs. A funnel underneath directs the dislodged bees back to the entrance of their hive.

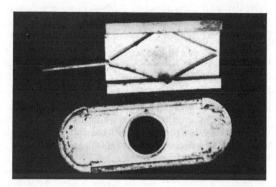

Fig. 169. *Dissembled Porter Bee Escape showing set of springs.*

Fig. 170. *Removing combs of honey by shaking and brushing method.*

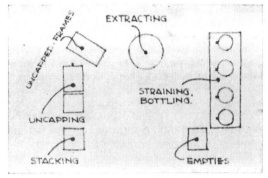

Fig. 171. *Diagram of set-out of honey house.*

Fig. 172. *Uncapping with cold knife over improvised vessel. Frame is tilted forward. Knife cuts in an upward direction.*

Fig. 173. *Uncapping with electrically heated knife. Frame is tilted forward. Knife cuts in a downward direction.*

Fig. 174. *Combs are selected by weight when loading extractor to minimise wobbling.*

Fig. 175. *Tangential extractor on wooden support secured by adjustable stays.*

Fig. 176. *Stand for extractor showing position of eye bolts.*

Processing

All extracting operations are facilitated if the honey is processed as soon as possible after it comes off the hives.

Setting the Stage

In small-scale beekeeping it will often be found that the laying out of apparatus and the clearing up afterwards entails more time and labour than the actual process of extracting, but great saving can be made by methodical lay-out of the processing. This can be detailed as stacking, uncapping, extracting, straining, settling and bottling *(Fig. 171)*.

Full supers should be stacked in a convenient position to allow minimum effort in lifting out individual combs onto the uncapping apparatus. For right-handed operators this position is on the left so that with little movement combs are grasped with both hands and swung into position over the uncapping tray.

Uncapping

Uncapping apparatus can vary in cost from a few pence to many pounds depending on the resources of the beekeeper and the amount of honey to be dealt with.

Improvised Uncapping Pail

A suitable uncapping receptacle for a small amount of honey can be made with an enamel pail *(Fig. 172)*. A piece of wood approximately ½-inch (12 mm.) thick and ¾-inch (19mm.) broad, of sufficient length to span the pail mouth, has a ¾-inch (19 mm.) nail driven through it to project about ¼-inch (6 mm.) and is then secured at both ends by wire, string or clamps to the flanges which carry the pail handle. Metal ends, if present on the honey combs, are removed and any brace comb attached to the wood parts chopped off to ensure that it can fit into the extractor cradle. The brace comb is much more conveniently disposed of at this stage than at any period when on a hive, and it will be noted that much of it consists of a large percentage of propolis. If wax prepared from cappings is to be used for show purposes, it is advisable to segregate this brace comb to avoid discolouring when rendering.

The end of the comb top bar is now placed on the nail point, which should dig slightly into the end wood to prevent slipping; the comb position ensures that cappings fall into the pail and not down the outside. The outer end of the top bar should be grasped with the left hand, the little and second fingers holding it in position and the weight of the arm forcing it firmly on to the nail point. The top bar should face the operator and the comb tilted to the right to form an acute angle with the wood support of about 70 degrees. The uncapping knife is now brought into play, starting at the bottom and cutting upwards. If the comb is tilted forward correctly, the cappings will fall away from the exposed honey surface until the knife severs the remaining cappings at the top, then the whole of the cappings should fall cleanly into the receptacle *(Fig. 172)*. If the comb is tilted backwards or held perpendicularly, the sheet of cappings is liable to fall back on to the honey surface, causing extra work in scraping off and giving trouble later when straining through an excess of wax particles being introduced into the honey. Once this first surface has been uncapped, a twisting motion with the left hand swivels the bar on its nail-point pivot, so that the bottom of the comb is now underneath the forearm, bringing the second surface into a convenient position to repeat uncapping.

Make combs suitable for future use

The method of uncapping super combs by cutting through the air space between honey and cappings is ideal, providing the combs are perfectly even, as the cappings slice off almost dry and are easily handled. When super combs have any unevenness, however, this method may prove to be a disadvantage, as the operator is forced to follow any undulations and on replacing the empty combs in supers, may find that they can only be returned to their original position and are more difficult to manipulate during future operations. When super comb has bulges or unevenness in any form it is preferable to run the uncapping knife through it with a straight, clean sweep close to the wood of the frame, producing even combs which can be inserted anywhere in the super and which will be drawn out during future nectar flows into well-shaped combs.

Occasionally combs are produced which have hollow areas of sealed honey so that the cappings are sunk well below the wood surface and it may be felt that such cells are not worth uncapping. This could be true as far as honey bulk is concerned, but if such areas are left they invariably prove a source of annoyance during future seasons, as adjacent combs may be drawn out to fill the resulting space. It is advisable, therefore, to uncap these surfaces where possible and if this cannot be done, to scrape the comb surface with the uncapping knife or suitable tool.

When the improvised pail fills so as to hinder uncapping, its contents can be emptied into the strainer part of a "ripener." "Ripener" is a misleading term applied to a tall, cylindrical container whose function is to store honey while it is settling. The degree of ripeness of honey is determined by its condition when removed from the hive. When a larger bulk of honey is to be dealt with, a receptacle having a screen through which honey can pass and a storage chamber fitted with a honey tap underneath, is superior. The various types of uncapping trays and pails on the market prove very satisfactory.

A piece of sticking-plaster wrapped round the little finger forms an effective barrier to the slight cuts whch may be received by the operator from the uncapping knife on its upward cutting motion.

A steam or electrically heated uncapping knife is a good investment for the larger beekeeper and it will be found easier, to use this appliance cutting down the surface of the comb instead of upwards, as with a cold uncapping knife *(Fig. 173)*.

Uncapped combs can be inserted directly into the extractor cage *(Fig. 174)* or if a large amount is to be dealt with, a temporary receptacle positioned on the operator's right-hand side allows uninterrupted uncapping.

Extracting

There are three kinds of extractor - tangential, radial and parallel, all with their respective merits. Combs are placed on the extremity of the revolving cage in a tangential extractor, in which position maximum efficiency is attained, which is of great value when dealing with very viscous honey. The disadvantage of this machine is that only one side of the comb is extracted at once and time is lost turning the partially extracted combs. In all extractors it is important to distribute the weight of combs evenly in the cages, otherwise great strain is put on the machines, which are apt to wobble about and be difficult to manage.

In the tangential extractor, care has to be taken to avoid bursting combs by applying too much force before the combs are nearly empty. Here, as the outer surfaces of the combs are being extracted, the heavier inside surfaces are pushed out by centrifugal force, which may result in the combs exploding outwards. The first surface should be extracted until two-thirds of the honey is removed, then the combs reversed and the second surface extracted fully before returning the original surface to the outside and completely emptying *(Fig. 177)*.

Radial and parallel extractors have the advantage of extracting both surfaces of the comb simultaneously, but again, even loading is essential and speed should be worked up gradually as the combs are being emptied.

With small amounts of honey, the extractor, when full, can be lifted onto a bench or table for emptying, but it will be found expedient to have it mounted on a firm base, allowing a container to be placed underneath the honey gate. This saves much heavy lifting, particularly if the operator is working single-handed. A simple, efficient and inexpensive base for the popular tangential extractor of six shallow or three deep comb capacity, can be made from two lengths of heavy timber, one half-checked at the end, the other half-checked in the centre and the two bolted together to form a flush T-shape. This is placed on three supports of wood or bricks and the extractor secured to it by its base and by three adjustable rods, which are hooked over the extractor rim and to eyebolts affixed near the extremities of the wooden T-base. By standing on the base, the operator adds weight to the stability of the apparatus *(Figs. 175 and 176)*. Honey from the extractor is now run directly into a strainer or carried to it in pails.

Avoid Bottlenecks

When honey is dense, or has been allowed to cool before extracting, a bottleneck is sometimes created at the strainer part of the "ripener" due to the accumulation of wax particles choking the mesh. Although it is possible to spoon out this blockage periodically - a tedious and messy job - much of it can be avoided by expedient handling of the honey from the extractor. Given time, wax particles will rise to the surface and the storage space at the bottom of the extractor should be taken full advantage of. When a large amount of honey is dealt with, much unwanted wax is introduced to the "ripener" strainer through the periodical complete emptying of the extractor. If the storage chamber is kept approximately three-quarters full, the weight of the honey will help to steady the extractor and many of the wax particles will remain floating on the surface. When the bulk of the honey has been strained into the "ripener", the residue of wax-clogged honey remaining in the extractor can now be emptied into the strainer to drain slowly away.

Straining

Straining can be accomplished by the use of an ordinary metal strainer, or, in addition, the honey can be passed through a double thickness of muslin or honey straining cloth. Some use fine-mesh nylon stockings with complete success, but when passed through any of these materials it is advantageous to have the honey slightly warmed.

Warming can be applied in various ways, but a simple, efficient and cheap form of heating can be applied by the use of plastic horticultural heating belts. These can be wound round containers and held in position with sellotape and because of the varying wattages obtainable, are extremely versatile. A plastic heating belt affixed to the bottom of the extractor not only warms the honey prior to straining, but also raises the temperature inside the extractor, which facilitates extraction *(Fig. 180)*.

It is at this juncture that the advantage of careful summer management can be seen, for if combs in the super have been kept strictly for honey storage, debris in the form of cocoon particles and pollen is absent and straining can be limited to the metal strainer. Here the only foreign matter is particles of wax, which are readily removed after straining and settling.

The strained honey should be allowed to settle in a warm temperature for two days. This allows minute wax particles and air bubnbles to rise to the surface, when they can be skimmed off and the honey is left clear and free from foreign matter.

Bottling

The ultimate form of presenting honey for disposal must now be considered and at time of writing the one-pound size honey jar with screw top lid is almost exclusively used. A certain amount of dust or "bloom" collects on jars even when new and if honey has to be shown to best advantage, all jars should be washed before filling. If, in a honey house or kitchen, two sinks or one sink and a washing machine, are present and a plentiful supply of really hot water is available, two operators can run through a gross of jars in ten minutes. Assuming both are right-handed, the stage can be set thus: boxes of unwashed jars are stacked on the extreme right hand side of operations and jars from them are placed into the right-hand sink, which is filled with hot water replenished from time to time as it cools or becomes dirty. The jars are now quickly washed - a plastic dish mop making an ideal tool for the job - then after a dozen or so have been cleaned, they are emptied and placed on their sides in the next sink, which is filled with a few inches of really hot water. A washing machine incorporating a heating element can be used to advantage in place of this second sink. A table or draining board is positioned either on the left or behind the operator when standing in front of the second sink and is furnished with two or three strips of wood about ¾-inch (19 mm.) square running the length of the surface. The heated jars are emptied and immediately placed upside-down so that their rims rest partly on the wood strips and partly on the table surface. Water is now able to run down the sides of the jars instead of forming a drip on the centre of the bases and the fact that they have been heated ensures complete drying-off in under one minute *(Fig. 181)*. The washed and dried jars are now returned to the cartons, which have been dusted and lined with clean newspaper and the surface of the table or draining board wiped down with a "Wetex" or "Spontex" cloth before the positioning of the next batch of washed and heated jars.

The advent of plastic containers which require no washing and a minimum storage space cuts down on labour costs, but they have not so far proved superior to glass containers in other ways.

Properties of Honey

Before discussing the final stages of preparing honey for disposal, let us examine some of its characteristics and in doing so, perhaps better understand why certain precautions have to be taken during its processing.

If honey is left in a shallow dish in a damp atmosphere for a few days, it will be seen to have increased its volume and will appear thin and watery. This is due to the hygroscopic property of honey which has absorbed water from the atmosphere and become diluted in the water it attracted to itself. If such diluted honey is left, yeast spores are able to develop and feed on the mixture, causing fermentation which is noticeable by a sour odour. Every effort should, therefore, be made to avoid introducing moisture to honey by removing only ripe honey from the hives, by storing combs of honey in a warm, dry atmosphere, by ensuring all apparatus, such as uncapping trays, extractors and "ripeners" are perfectly dry before use, and by keeping all extracted honey sealed in air-tight containers.

Honey is derived from the breaking down of complex sugar found in nectar by the bees' digestive enzymes into simple sugars, mainly dextrose (glucose) and levulose (fructose). Honey will crystalise or "granulate" quickly or slowly depending on the ratio of these sugars present. Granulation is simply the crystallisation of the dextrose sugar, which is enveloped in a film of the non-crystal forming levulose. Raspberry honey in particular is a good example of a high-dextrose content honey and it may granulate in or out of the comb in a matter of weeks after gathering. A partial shrinkage takes place when granulation occurs and in a jar, an air space or vacuum is sometimes created between the honey and the glass. This in no way spoils the honey, but the patchy appearance, termed "frosting" detracts from the sales appeal of the finished article.

The source of honey and marketing conditions influence the producer's choice of packing it in either fluid or granulated form. It so often happens that beautifully-prepared, clear honey remains on the retailer's shelves for a period of several months, then begins to granulate. Sometimes this natural granulation turns out quite soft and fine, but at other times a hard, coarse, or partial granulation results, which again, while not detracting from the food value, nevertheless may not appeal to the eye of a prospective customer *(Fig. 178)*.

Fig. 177. *Comb on the right properly extracted. Comb on the left has burst outward as too much force had been applied before reversing.*

Fig. 178. *Honey allowed to granulate without control.*

Fig. 179. *Tank of honey being skimmed using plastic bowl scraper and cream skimmer.*

Fig. 180. *A plastic soil heater can be used to heat honey tanks or extractor.*

Fig. 181. *Jars are washed, dipped into very hot water, then tilted upside down on ¾ inch wood strips to drain and dry off.*

Fig. 182. *Labelling granulated honey jars. A moist "Wetex" kitchen cloth is ideal for wetting gummed labels.*

Fig. 183 *Honey comb cut through showing cells are not horizontal.*

Fig. 184. *Cut comb heather honey can be wrapped in plain dry cellophane.*

It is possible to delay granulation by heating for half an hour at 120deg.F (49deg.C), but much foresight in marketing conditions and knowledge of the honey sources are required to guarantee a lasting effect. Moreover, honey, once heated, may granulate with an even coarser granule than would occur without such treatment. Honey which is likely to be consumed within a few months of bottling can be put up for sale in fluid form, but properly granulated honey will remain stable for years and is a better commercial proposition.

Small quantities of granulated honey in jars can be liquified in a domestic, microwave oven. Remove metal lids. For four 1lb. jars, setting is "defrost" for 35 minutes.

Controlled Granulation

A fine-grained, granulated honey, reasonably soft in texture and free from excess "frosting" in the jars can be obtained by controlled granulation using the following method.

After honey has settled in the "ripeners" the scum of fine wax particles is skimmed off, a plastic bowl scraper and cream skimmer being employed for the purpose. The film of scum is manipulated towards the middle of the honey surface using the plastic scraper with a painting motion, then the cream skimmer is gently inserted beneath the scum mass, which is quickly lifted and emptied into a suitable container. *(Fig. 179)*. This process may have to be repeated until a perfectly clear surface remains. Depending on the crystals initially forming in a mass of honey, the whole bulk will granulate in the same form as these crystals. Thus it is desirable to start off a batch of granulating honey with crystals of a known fine texture. This can be accomplished by introducing some selected granulated honey kept over in jars or tins from previous years, such an addition being termed a "starter" or "primer". A quarter to half a pound of this primer is dropped into a suitable mixer, such as a piston and jar type egg beater, along with an equal amount of fluid honey from the "ripener", and the whole beaten up till a creamy-like consistency is achieved. This mixture is then introduced to the container holding the current season's fluid honey.

Some means of ensuring that granulation is forming evenly throughout the honey bulk is necessary, otherwise a cone of granulation is liable to form at the base of the container. A gentle stirring every day with a wooden shaft or a milk mixer will keep the whole contents uniform. Depending on temperature, dextrose content of the honey, and amount of primer used, the honey will eventually change into a creamy mass resembling thin gruel within a few days to several weeks. At this stage it must be bottled immediately, otherwise within a few days the mass solidifies and would require to be partially reliquified before handling.

As the honey has been primed with a fine-grained crystal and as partial shrinkage has already occurred, the resultant product has both good keeping-qualities and sales appeal. Such honey, if of good quality at the onset, can remain in the retailer's stocks for years without signs of deterioration.

An alternative method, which can save labour at a time when it can least be spared, such as during a heavy extracting period, can give a softer granulation, but the total labour involved at a later date is much greater. The honey is skimmed and primed as before, but after a few days it is drawn off into honey tins then sealed and stored. When a batch is required for bottling, the tins are partially immersed in hot water, or placed in a carefully controlled heating cabinet or oven until approximately one-third of the contents is re-liquified. It will be found that the liquid honey occupies the perimeter of the tin and that the remaining "solid" honey has been reduced to a mushy texture. The contents of one or more tins are now emptied into a suitable container and the mass pulped and stirred until a creamy consistency is reached, when the mixture is bottled immediately. Although it is possible to further soften the honey by vigorous beating, such a form being termed "creamed honey", its keeping-qualities are impaired due to the amount of air incorporated, but this may prove a popular product where quick consumption is anticipated.

All extracted honey offered for retail sale is required by law to be labelled with certain information. The net weight of the jars' content must be stated, the word "honey" must be included and the name and address of the producer or packer must appear. An attractive label does much to enhance the finished product. When gummed labels are used, a soaked "Wetex" type cloth is an ideal bed for wetting the labels prior to fixing. *(Fig. 182)*.

Section Honey.

The preparation of section honey for marketing is less involved than for extracted honey, nevertheless it should be attended to with care. Any adhering propolis or brace comb should be scraped off with a sharp knife, attention being taken to prevent scrapings from falling on to the face of the comb. The use of plastic covers over the section crates when on the hives does much to prevent excess of both propolis and brace comb.

Wrapping sections involves a little extra labour, but this not only imparts a better sales appeal, but also improves the keeping-qualities. Cellophane wrappers are obtainable, either plain or with attractive margins and printing. After soaking in a bowl of warm water, the wrappers are placed as required on a smooth, even surface such as provided by a plastic-topped table and the inside surface wiped with a "Wetex" type cloth to remove excess water. Where printed wrappers are used it is necessary to ensure the printing is on the outside and the correct way up in relation to the position of the section as it is to be displayed or stored. A cleaned section is placed in position on the wrapper and a few daubs of gum arabic applied to the wood before the cellophane is neatly wrapped round and finally sealed with further touches of the gum brush. Some prefer to allow the wrapper to dry out on the section then seal the joints with cellophane tape. When the cellophane dries out it shrinks and gives a clean, tidy, glazed appearance to the finished section, which not only looks appealing, but also excludes dust, insects and dampness.

A further improvement can be made by incorporating a band of coloured or tartan paper, the same width as the section wood. This is affixed before applying the wrapper. When the cellophane shrinks, the paper is drawn over part of the wood edge giving a very pleasing effect.

Weeping.

If a piece of honey comb is cut through at right angles to the mid-rib, it will be seen that the cells do not run horizontally, but take a slight slope upwards. *(Fig. 183)*. This assists in retaining the honey in its cell and prevents the surface of the honey from having direct contact with the wax capping. If the comb is inverted or laid on its side, honey is liable to flow downwards and rest on the wax capping. Because of the hygroscopic property of honey, moisture is attracted to the outside of the cappings and is sometimes seen to accumulate and discolour the comb. Such disfigurement is termed "weeping".

It is, therefore, necessary to store or display section honey so that the cells tilt upwards, in other words, keep them in the same position as when they were built in the hive. Such procedure can be simplified by always ensuring that sections are placed in the same way throughout the apiary. Depending on the type chosen, the split side for "split-and-grooved" sections and the middle split for "split-three-way" sections should always be on top.

Storage of comb in damp conditiona also causes "weeping." Therefore, sections should be stored in airtight containers in a dry atmosphere.

Dealing with Cappings.

Where a small amount of cappings has to be dealt with, a convenient method is to put them into an empty "ripener" along with two or three pails of rain or soft water, stir thoroughly and allow to settle for a day or two. The water and honey solution can then be drained slowly from the honey gate, but it is advisable to use a tap strainer to catch pieces of wax which may flow out. This solution of honey and water can be fed to bees or can be used for mead making and the cappings should then be thoroughly dried before rendering. A heather-honey press can be usefully employed for squeezing honey out of wet cappings if the amount justifies it. Alternatively, allow bees to clean them up. A suitable method for this is to use a cappings cleaner, which is placed in much the same way as a feeder on the top of a strong hive.

Cappings and apparatus sticky with honey may be cleaned up by allowing bees to rob them outside but several precautions must be taken. Exposed honey should never be placed near an apiary containing stocks of different strengths, for instance, strong colonies and nuclei, as there is every possibility that when the honey is cleaned up, the strong may rob the weak. Exposed honey should not be placed near a hive, but at least 100 yards away, and allowed to be cleaned up completely before removing the clean cappings or apparatus.

Heather Honey.

Ling heather honey has the property of being thixotropic, that is, it is a natural jelly, but on agitation becomes a fluid, returning to the jelly state when allowed to settle. Because of this characteristic, heather honey requires to be treated somewhat differently from other honeys produced in this country, as it cannot be extracted by centrifugal force in the normal manner. It is necessary either to crush the comb or apply some form of agitation to render it into a fluid state before extracting. The crushing or pressing of comb, although considered rather wasteful, is still widely practised and the various heather honey presses on the market prove quite satisfactory. There are, however, alternative methods of preparing the comb before pressing.

Pressing heather honey involves a wastage of drawn comb and although wax is salvaged at a later stage, the beekeeper may be deprived of the very valuable commodity of a supply of drawn comb for use the following season. For this reason, many consider the agitation and extracting methods superior.

The perfor extractor is a tool which proves reasonably efficient, but the labour involved in its use restricts it to the beekeeper with only a few stocks. A comb of heather honey is uncapped in the usual way, then laid flat onto a special holding rack. The perfor extractor, which consists of a number of rigid needles set in a wood block, is now pressed over the comb so that the needles pierce the midrib, and waggled from side to side. This process is repeated all over both faces of the comb, the agitation of the needles renderng the honey temporarily fluid, which is then extracted in an ordinary extractor. Any comb containing pollen should be excluded otherwise when the needles are withdrawn, patches of pollen-filled comb are liable to be torn away.

The Norwegian and French honey looseners are becoming increasingly popular with the larger-scale beekeeper, for although the initial cost is heavy, the saving in labour and drawn comb is considered well justified. This apparatus consists of a number of heavy pins, so spaced that an area of comb is covered by their points. When pressure is applied they are so loosely set in their framework that although penetration into the honey is achieved, the midrib is not pierced. As with the perfor extractor, the combs are uncapped then laid on a moving stage which positions the comb, an area at a time, under the undulating pins. When the combs have been passed backwards and forwards, the other face is exposed and the process repeated. The loosened or agitated honey is then extracted in a tangential extractor.

In all methods of obtaining run heather honey it is desirable, indeed, often essential, to work under a high temperature - 90 deg.F (32 deg.C) being not too high and as a further aid, combs can be pre-heated for several hours before operations. This can be done in a heated room or in a specially insulated heating cabinet, care being taken to prevent the temperature from exceeding 100 deg.F (38 deg.C) otherwise the comb is rendered so soft that it may collapse.

Heather honey can be produced in a "fluid", "granulated", or "creamed" state, the remarks already made about light honeys being equally applicable. One exception, however, applies to the heating of granulated honey in tins prior to partial creaming. Heather honey, if over-heated, becomes "carmelised", giving it a most unpleasant appearance and flavour. Carmelisation is caused by the solidification of the protein colloids which are present in ling heather honey and give it its thixotropic quality. Comparison may be made with the change in the albumen or white when an egg is boiled. To avoid this it should not be heated above 145 deg. F (63 deg. C) for longer than 30 minutes, then it should be cooled as rapidly as possible, the sealed tins being placed in a bath of cold running water.

The simplest, but most wasteful method is to produce the comb on unwired foundation, then after the crop is removed, the honey comb is simply cut out of the frames, *(Fig. 185)*, placed in a suitable cloth and pressure applied. A fairly satisfactory method is to scrape the honey comb from the foundation into a straining cloth lining a plastic pail, then, according to the capacity of the honey press, the edges of the cloth are folded upwards and tied to form a "dumpling". This is pressed in the usual way. *(Fig. 188)*. A Smith scraper is employed as follows: the tightened wire side is inserted into the honey comb at the top of the comb when held perpendicularly, and using steady pressure the wire is guided downwards, cutting the comb as it goes. *(Fig. 186)*. Depending on the size of the combs used, two or more cuts have to be made, then the tool is reversed and the scraper side used to scrape down the severed comb. *(Fig. 187)*. It is advisable not to scrape the comb hard down to the foundation, but to leave an ⅛th inch (3 mm) or so of cell walls protruding, otherwise the foundation, when inserted the following year, is liable to be gnawed down in places by bees. Honey remaining on the scraped foundation is in a fluid state due to the agitation of cutting and scraping and it can be removed by immediate extracting in a centrifugal extractor.

Cut Comb Honey.

Much skill, experience and apparatus are necessary for dealing with run heather honey and many small-scale beekeepers do not consider such processing worthwhile. Fortunately there is a growing demand for "cut comb" or "package" honey and good-quality ling heather honey lends itself ideally for this. The production of such honey has already been commented upon, but there are a few points to note in handling the finished crop.

The combs are cut out of the frame or "cog" with a sharp knife and carefully laid on a clean, flat surface. There are many and varied methods of cutting and shaping the pieces of comb, ranging from the use of a knife to very efficient cutting boxes. *(Figs. 189-190)*. A very simple but effective piece of apparatus consists of a wooden base with two uprights, over which is stretched a taut wire. The comb is lifted over the wire and gently lowered over the position where the cut is desired. Odd-shaped pieces of comb and patches of unsealed honey should be set to one side for pressing and the operator should endeavour to keep the pieces of cut comb as square-cornered and as uniform as possible. The comb should not be bruised or otherwise damaged and convenient sizes of cut comb are in the region of four ounces in weight. The cut comb is now placed on a suitable draining board - a cake cooling screen or wire queen excluder serves the purpose - and allowed to drain in a warm temperature for a few hours. *(Fig. 191)*. Plain cellophane sheeting is cut into suitable sizes and the cut comb neatly wrapped in it, the edges being stuck with gum arabic or cellotape. Unlike the wrapping of sections, the cellophane should be used dry. *(Fig. 184)*.

As an alternative method, cartons are used for cut comb honey, which have great sales appeal and cut down labour

Fig. 185 *Cutting out a complete comb of Heather Honey is sometimes thought to be wasteful.*

Fig. 186 *The taut wire side of a "Smith" scraper is drawn down the comb fairly close to the midrib.*

Fig. 187 *The "Smith" scrapper is reversed and the severed honey comb is scraped into a pressing cloth draped over a plastic pail.*

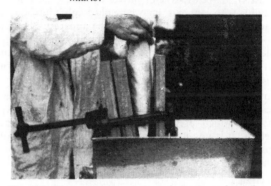

Fig. 188 *The scraped or cut comb is secured in the pressing cloth and inserted for pressing.*

Fig. 189 *A comb from an eke is lowered into a cutting box. Taut wires cut the comb into suitably sized pieces.*

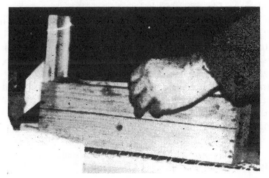

Fig. 190 *A cheese wire severs the comb from the wooden slat.*

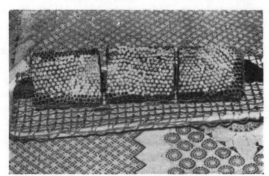

Fig. 191 *The cut comb is drained on a grid.*

Fig. 192 *Attractive cartons are a popular container for cut-comb honey.*

considerably *(Fig. 192).* One minor drawback is that the cut comb must conform in shape to the chosen carton, which may result in a slightly higher degree of comb wastage.

In all cut comb honey offered for retail sale it is advisable to prepare it as near as possible to the time of likely consumption, as the cut cells may show signs of granulation, which detract from its appearance. Combs should be kept in bulk whole and only cut and packaged immediately prior to sale.

Rendering Wax.

Once wax cappings or brace combs have been cleaned of honey by bees, or by washing, it is necessary to refine it before offering it for sale or part-exchange to the appliance dealers.

The "M.G.", Wax Extractor proves extremely satisfactory for dealing with cappings, but where old comb is introduced, the cloth strainer is apt to clog and the apparatus cease to function. Where top-quality wax is required, soft water only should be used, otherwise contact with lime is apt to discolour the product. The moulds used should be wider at their rim than at their base to facilitate removal.

Although old brood combs contain a certain amount of wax, this can only be efficiently removed by large, pressure-type extractors, which are beyond the reach of the average beekeeper. It is not considered worth while saving such old combs and they should be disposed-off quickly to avoid them becoming a breeding ground for wax moths.

Marketing.

The marketing of surplus honey often presents a problem, especially to the smaller beekeeper who, in a glut year, panic-sells his crop for ridiculously low prices. It is wise policy to come to an agreement with the retailer to supply him with quality produce at as consistent a price as possible. In this way the customer gets to know a brand which can be relied upon. Beekeepers are more fortunte than most food producers in that their product has keeping-qualities and in a glut year it is an easy matter to store part of the crop in bulk and release it when the market is scarce. Good-quality honey, properly stored, will keep for many years without any signs of deterioration.

Storage of Combs.

After the season's final extracting some thought must now be given to the storing of the empty combs and the rendering and disposal of the accumulated wax derived from brace comb and cappings.

Empty, extracted combs have the metal ends returned to them, those which were previously spaced on narrow metal ends can be fitted with wide ones at this point, if they are well and evenly drawn, then placed in supers. Some prefer to store combs in the wet condition, that is, having the remains of the honey still adhering. The advantages claimed are that the comb is not so liable to damage from wax moth larvae and the honey-filmed comb is more attractive to bees when put on stocks the following season. Whilst this may be true, such procedure is messy and if ideal storage conditions are not available, the honey remaining often becomes sour due to its hygroscopic characteristic.

The alternative method of storing combs dry necessitates the cleaning of them by bees on top of stocks. The supers of extracted, wet combs are placed over the crown board, which has the feed hole left open and precautions taken to prevent robbing, by restricting entrances of hives and using screen boards over the supers. Five or six such supers can be added to a powerful stock, which will clean up the loose honey in a few days if the temperature is sufficiently high. It sometimes happens that instead of all the honey being transferred down to the brood chambers, it is collected on a few combs in the centre of the bottom super. Such combs can be collected in one or two supers and stored separately or, to avoid this situation developing, an empty super is placed on the crown board before the supers of wet combs are added. The bees dislike leaving a space between stores in the hive and normally remove every drop of honey to the brood chamber. The supers of dry, empty combs can be cleared of bees by the use of Porter escapes, or by waiting for a cold morning or evening when they are deserted. The supers of combs are then stacked in suitable storage accommodation, using queen excluders, screen boards or spare crown boards top and bottom of each stack to exclude mice.

Co-operative Arrangements.

There have been some very effective developments in honey-handling over the past few decades. The Norwegian "Sjolies" loosening machine has made the centrifugal extraction of heather honey a commercial possibility, and when it is used in conjunction with a modern semi-radial, power-driven extractor, maximum efficiency is assured.

Power-driven rotary filters which deal very effectively with heather honey after extraction are available, and to deal with oil-seed-rape honey even after granulation, there are food-processing machines capable of filtering-out wax particles at 1500 RPM. Various uncapping machines - both semi and fully automatic, can alleviate much of the tedium in some honey-house operations.

Unfortunately the cost of these machines is well out of the reach of beekeepers running less than fifty stocks. Even medium-scale commercial-opertors would not be in a position to justify the purchase of the most efficient equipment.

There is however, the possibility of smaller beekeepers having access to such labour-saving and efficient equipment in several ways. One is "contract-extracting" whereby the beekeeper pays so much per pound or per super to have the work done by a large-scale beekeeper who already has suitable equipment installed. There is also the concept of several beekeepers clubbing together to form a co-operative or syndicate arrangement which can take many forms, from a simple communal extractor to a separate building to house more elaborate equipment.

Details of such large scale honey-handling is contained in a booklet entitled "Co-operative honey handling and extracting techniques" - Bulletin No. 30, published by the Scottish Agricultural Colleges.

CHAPTER XV.

ENEMIES OF BEES.

Influences detrimental to the honey bee colony can be divided into three groups. They are mineral, vegetable and animal.

The Dangers of Chemicals.

The ill effects of dampness in hives during winter have already been discussed and up till a few decades ago, this excess of moisture was the only non-organic substance a beekeeper had to contend with. The advent of the chemical control of weeds and insects, however, has set a vast and complex problem to apiculture and has radically changed the pattern of beekeeping in many parts of the country. Many wild plants which afforded a good source of pollen and nectar are now so reduced that bees derive little sustenance from these one-time sources.

Although chemical weed-killers do not normally destroy bees directly, there are occasions particularly during spring months, when heavy casualties occur. At this time of year foraging bees have a limited flying range and if such spraying is carried out in the vicinity, bees may come in direct contact with the chemical or it may be transmitted through water and pollen. Affected stocks often have a carpet of dead or dying bees at the hive entrances and beekeepers have confused the signs with those of Acarine disease. Generally the stock recovers but the depletion of the foraging force often puts paid to honey surplus.

Chemical insect control has a more direct bearing on the problem and reports of casualties in bee colonies have successively grown over the past few years. Although it may be difficult, or even impossible, to observe the direct consequences of chemical spray in the apiaries at times, the effects of many of these chemicals can have far-reaching implications, not always apparent at the time. Many foraging bees die away from the hive after being in contact with chemical sprays, but sometimes the effects can be seen at the hive entrances.

Affected bees often reel about in circles, with extended tongues, or fall on their backs, usually keeping up a loud buzzing. In severe cases the poison is transmitted to brood, the appearance of which is not unlike chilled brood, and infected pollen can be a lasting source of trouble.

Cases of poisoning have occurred due to the use of foundation, frames and other hive parts which had been placed in a store treated with insecticide against pests such as moths or woodworm.

The greatest danger to bees arises when they are actually working on the crop being treated so that the chemical spray has direct contact with the insect. This situation should not occur if spraying technique for insect control is carried out properly, for most crops should be treated before and after flowering period and weed control should be carried out long before the plants have reached the flowering stage. Unfortunately, due to weather and contract spraying, these conditions are not always met, which causes detrimental results both to the crops and to bee colonies. *(Fig. 193).*

Wild mustard or charlock is a weed which is often sprayed during open blossom and because of the likelihood of such bad husbandry, this possible nectar source should be treated with caution. A complication arises in fruit growing areas where trees are sprayed. Although this may be performed outwith the blossoming period, spray is liable to fall on sources immediately attractive to bees. Dandelions present danger in this instance, for they often flower under and around fruit trees in early spring.

A sound knowledge of locality again proves invaluable, for a beekeeper should be able to ascertain in advance what crops are likely to be sprayed and a friendly liaison with the farmers or fruit growers can do much to minimise the trouble. It can

often be arranged that spraying is done at a time of day when bees are not flying, or a day chosen when, because of inclement weather, bees are unlikely to leave their hives. If prior warning of spraying is given, a beekeeper has the choice of moving his stocks temporarily from the district, or confining his charges to their hives. In the latter case, an empty super containing a suitable feeder of water should be given above the brood chambers and screen board and entrance block affixed as for moving bees. During the day, hives shold be kept shaded and the roofs placed cornerwise over the screen board. Various forms of enclosures made from hessian or plastic netting to form bee-proof tents designed to shut-in stocks, have been tested, but none have proved satisfactory. Released bees simply fly to the available light or air source and form clusters until they fall exhausted to the ground.

VEGETABLE FOES.

Some species of plants and trees, while not causing harm to bee colonies, can, nevertheless, be a source of irritation to the beekeeper. In Southern counties the privet at times secretes a nectar whch is unpalatable to the human taste and more widely, though fortunately more sparsely distributed, ragwort can impart a most unpleasant taste and aroma to other honeys.

In hot, dry seasons, the presence of some trees, notably beech and oak, can impair the quality of the honey crop, as bees may collect honey dew from these sources. Honey dew is derived from the activities of aphids feeding on certain host trees and plants and although it can be used by bees without apparent ill-effect, the appearance and flavour of this substance does not appeal to the human palate. Honey dew is dark in colour and has the appearance of a strong tea infusion when stored in open cells. Judicious selection of combs prior to extracting can do much to prevent undesirable honeys and honey dew from tainting the bulk of the season's honey crop.

Certain species of rhododendron secrete a nectar which is poisonous to bees and whole apiaries have been reported devastated from this cause. *(Fig. 194).* Fortunately such occurrences are rare and it is only in exceptional years that this trouble is experienced. If poisoning is suspected from this source, confining or moving stocks in the same way as for chemical spray precautions, should be considered.

Various vegetable moulds are present in bee stocks, some of which can cause considerable damage when conditions are conducive to them. These moulds can damage combs and hive parts, *(Fig.197),* cause mouldy pollen (bettsia alvei) and even attack brood and adult bees.

Chalk Brood (Ascosphaera apis)

Chalk Brood attacks the bee larva usually just after sealing and transforms it into a rubber-like mummy which subsequently becomes hard, brittle and white in appearance - hence the name. *(Fig. 195-196).* It is often difficult to distinguish between Chalk Brood and mouldy pollen at first glance, but the dead larvae are easily removed from their cells and on close inspection the partially developed head and thorax is often seen. In most parts of Scotland this malady can be found in almost every apiary, if a close inspection of brood combs is made, but fortunately it never appears to reach serious proportions. It is known, however, that in Southern parts, Chalk Brood can cause greater damage. It is suspected that Chalk Brood is more prevalent in apiaries where intensive brood spreading is carried out.

The keeping of strong stocks and the provision of ample ventilation helps to prevent the spread of this trouble and the destruction of affected combs in severe cases effects a cure.

Stone Brood (Aspergillus flavus) Yellow Green
　　　　　　(Aspergillus fumigatus) Grey Green

Stone Brood is another malady caused by a mould which turns affected larvae into a hard, greenish-coloured residue. It is rare in this country and a cure has not so far been prescribed. The precautions relating to Chalk Brood would, no doubt, be of considerable advantage in any treatment attempted.

Addled Brood

There are a number of conditions which can exist in a bee colony, which are not strictly speaking diseases, but can result in the death or malformation of the developing brood. One of these conditions is addled brood, *(Fig. 198)*, which is caused by a defective queen and is thought to occur through some genetic fault. Larvae, pupae and even unhatched adults can be affected and the remedy is simply to requeen the stock.

Malnutrition through a shortage of pollen can cause a condition similar in appearance to addled brood and many previous cases diagnosed as addled brood may well have been sac brood or shrimp brood.

Bald-Headed Brood

This is a fairly rare malady said to be caused by the presence of wax moth larvae tunnelling in the brood comb and the subsequent attempts of the bees to reach and remove them. In their zeal, adult bees uncap and expose the bare heads of the developing pupae and do not seal them up again. *(Fig. 199)*. Many of the exposed pupae develop normally, but some become malformed if there is a heavy infestation of wax moth present, the excreta from these larvae causing the damage.

Chilled Brood

When a beekeeper has been practising brood spreading at inopportune times, or has neglected to ensure adequate bees are present to cover a given amount of brood, such as when making nuclei, brood may become chilled and die. The appearance of chilled brood is easily recognised, as brood in all stages is usually affected. The young larvae especially assume a very dark colour. Combs containing chilled brood can be cleared up by introducing them to a powerful stock.

ANIMAL ADVERSARIES.

The animal kingdom - and in this is included bacteria - causes the most varied and destructive maladies of the bee colony. These maladies can be subdivided into two categories - those which affect the brood and those affecting adult bees. We will deal with the brood diseases first.

European Foul Brood (Streptococcus Pluton)

E.F.B. is caused by a miscroscopic organism which is transmitted to the bee larvae via the infected mouth parts of young nurse bees and through smears left in brood cells. The larvae are attacked, usually before sealing, and assume a twisted and melted-down appearance. *(Fig. 200)*. Other bacteria already present in the hive further decompose the remains until only a dried-up scale, which is easily removed, is left. E.F.B. is usually associated with weak colonies and is most prevalent in early summer, often disappearing after a heavy nectar flow.

Climatic or geographical conditions appear to have much influence on the development of E.F.B. as it is virtually non-existent in Scotland, whereas it causes much concern in parts of Southern England. European Foul Brood is not confined to the continent of Europe, likewise American Foul Brood did not originate in, nor is it confined to America. The names were given by G.F. White, one of the pioneers in the isolation of the bacteria.

Destruction of heavily infected colonies and the feeding, in syrup, of Terramycin (1 gram per pound of syrup) to slightly infected colonies, is the accepted method of treatment.

American Foul Brood (Bacillus larvae)

A.F.B. is caused by a bacteria which attacks and kills the larva after sealing and reduces the remains, firstly to a dark, slimy mass, then in later stages, to a dried-up scale which adheres firmly to the cell base and wall. Affected cells present a dark greasy appearance, the cappings are sunken and in advanced cases may also be perforated. *(Fig. 201)*. When a match stick is inserted into an active A.F.B. infected cell and slowly withdrawn, the contents adhere to the match and stretch out an inch or so. This "ropiness" test is generally infallible but can be checked upon by microscopic examination. *(Fig. 202)*.

Spread of A.F.B. within the Hive. To follow the spread of A.F.B. within a stock, let us imagine what happens when a stock has one diseased cell in its brood nest. A young scavenger bee attempts to clean out the infected debris and in doing so, gets her mouth parts contaminated with spores of the bacteria. It will be remembered that, at a later stage in her life, this young bee will become a nurse and in carrying out this duty, transmits the spores from her mouth parts to other larvae. More larvae are, therefore infected and when their remains are cleared up by more scavenger bees, an ever-increasing number of larvae become infected.

Alternatively, a scavenger bee with infected mouth parts becomes a house bee, receiving nectar from the returning foragers and storing it in honey cells either in supers or brood chambers. As A.F.B. spores are not destroyed by contact with honey, although they do not develop in this medium, they may lie dormant over many years until fed to a bee larva, when they can develop and spread again.

Climatic conditions and locality again appear to influence the development of a disease, for in some districts A.F.B. spreads within a stock fairly rapidly, while in others the spread is barely perceptible over a period of several years. It has been demonstrated that a disease-resistant strain of bee which shows vigorous cell cleaning tendencies is not so prone to extinction by an attack of A.F.B.

Spread of A.F.B. between Colonies. How then does A.F.B. spread from colony to colony, or for that matter, from apiary to apiary, and why does a powerful stock of bees suddenly show signs of infection in its comb?

When a colony has been infected for some time, more and more cells are affected and less and less young bees hatch. As a result the colony dwindles in strength until it either dies out completely, or is rendered so weak that it is incapable of repelling robber bees from outside sources. Robbing bees from stocks in the same apiary, or from stocks situated in an apiary some distance away, carry the honey from the vanquished stock back to their own hives. *(Fig. 203)*. Spores of A.F.B. are carried in this honey, or on the robbers' mouth parts, and when contact is made with larvae in those otherwise healthy colonies, the disease gains a new foothold. Although hives which have remained derelict and empty over many years may not appear to be attractive to robber bees, the danger of infection remains if the colony had succumbed to A.F.B. A stray swarm may enter such a hive, take possession of the old combs and remain in the hive for some time. Such a swarm may not survive for long as the brood is destroyed by the disease, but a certain amount of honey is sure to be stored in the comb, which, after the death of the swarm, again becomes a source of attraction to robbers and, therefore, a source of infection.

It will be noted that strong stocks of bees are most prone to attempt robbing and as it is these strong stocks which are maintained by the most competent beekeepers, it follows that their stocks are the ones most likely to be affected should A.F.B. be present in an area.

Precautions. The robbing of diseased colonies is one way in which A.F.B. can be spread, but there are many others by which a beekeeper can unwittingly introduce it to the apiary. Hive tools, smokes, gloves, rollers, clothing - even the beekeepers person can be the means of transmitting spores. Stringent measures have to be taken to clean these items if

Fig. 193 Spraying machine in action. The greatest danger arises when bees are working on the area.

Fig. 194. Some species of rhododendron are poisonous to bees.

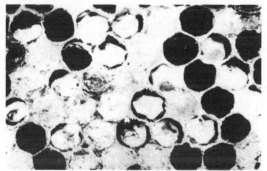

Fig. 195. Appearance of brood attacked by the vegetable mould chalk brood. (Ascophaera Apis).
(Photo. MAFF)

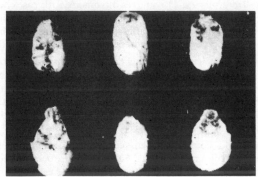

Fig. 196. "Mummies" destroyed by chalk brood removed from cells. (Photo. MAFF)

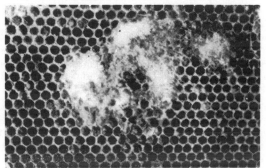

Fig. 197. Mould can cause deteriation of comb and hive parts.

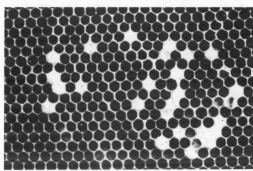

Fig. 198. Addled brood can be caused by pollen shortage or defective queen.

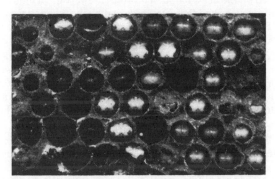

Fig. 199. Bald-headed brood said to be caused by wax moth larvae.

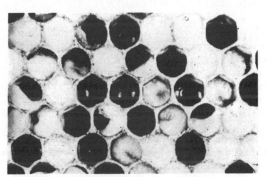

Fig. 200. Larvae attacked by European foul brood. (Streptococcus Pluton). (Photo. MAFF)

they have been in contact with the disease before using them in a healthy apiary. Scrubbing and thoroughly washing-off all stickiness with several changes of water should be carried out.

The direct transferring of combs or supers from infected stocks is an obvious cause of spread but what is often missed is that second-hand equipment may have had contact with such stocks. Second-hand equipment should not be bought-in to existing apiaries unless the history of the vendor's apiary is well known *(Fig. 205)*.

Honey and honey-house equipment is another possible source of contamination. Honey from unknown sources including imported honey shuld never be fed to bee-colonies and those in charge of communal extracting equipment should satisfy themselves that honey-comb for processing comes only from disease-free apiaries. The sources of some A.F.B. cases have been traced to honey-tins which had contained imported honey and had been discarded out-of-doors by manufacturing-bakers, so that foraging bees had access to them *(Fig. 204)*.

Migratory beekeepers should check on the history of other beekeepers when using communal apiary sites. A stock weak from A.F.B. could easily be robbed out in such circumstances and the robbing colonies could be the means of distributing the disease over a wide area when returned to their home apiaries.

When brood combs are being examined throughout the season, careful scrutiny should be given to any cells not conforming to a regular brood pattern. Any sealed cells left after those beside them have hatched, should be pierced with a match-stick. Usually they will be found to contain old honey, pollen or even Chalk brood in which case there is no problem, but this routine check could detect the presence of A.F.B. in its early stages.

Dealing with A.F.B. Until The Bee Disease Control Order of 1982 was enacted, beekeepers in Scotland were permitted to treat all brood diseases in their apiaries as they thought fit and from the late nineteen-forties until 1982, some used antibiotics against A.F.B. Undoubtedly sulphathiazole, when applied carefully, was very successful not only in controlling A.F.B. but eliminating it in some districts.

Unfortunately the drug did not kill the spore form of the disease so that if the treatment was only partly or haphazardly administered, the active, therefore recognisable form of A.F.B. was suppressd but latent spores remained. These spores could be released and re-activated, sometimes years later, and stocks so treated, could be the means of transmitting the disease to other parts of the country.

With the run-down of the Scottish Beekeeping Advisory Services, there were not sufficient funds to supervise chemotherapy treatments, and when the cost of labour and material was taken into consideration, it was felt that these treatments should discontinue. It is now an offence "except by an authorised person to treat any bees with any substance which may have the effect of disguising the presence of, or rendering difficult the detection of, American foul brood or European foul brood". This of course prohibits the use of sulphathiazole for treating stocks showing signs of A.F.B. It should be noted that only authorised persons may administer the chemotherapy treatment for European foul brood.

The "Notifiable Diseases of Bees" are A.F.B., E.F.B. and Varroatosis. If a beekeeper or person in charge of bees, suspects that any of these conditions are present in any stocks, he or she is legally required to notify the responsible authority of the fact. In England and Wales, the authority is the Ministry of Agriculture, Fisheries and Food, in Scotland, the Department of Agriculture for Scotland and in Ulster, the Department of Agriculture for Northern Ireland. There is however, nothing to stop a beekeeper from calling-in expert opinion to verify or otherwise, such suspicions before notifying the authorities.

Normally if a case of A.F.B. was verified by an apiary inspection, sample combs would be taken by the representative of the authority for laboratory examination. If found positive, a destruction notice would be served on the beekeeper and arrangements made for the destruction of the infected colonies. This should be carried out in the evening when bees have ceased flying for the day. A cloth soaked in petrol, applied to the hive entrance, will prevent the escape of any bees *(Fig. 206),* then about a pint of petrol is poured over the frame-tops, the fumes quickly killing the inmates *(Fig. 207)*. The contents of the hive are then carefully removed and placed in a hole, four to six feet deep, previously dug in the ground nearby, and the material destroyed by fire. When destruction is completed, the hole is filled in and the ground trampled firmly back in place. If the hive is in poor condition, it can be burned at the same time, but if considered worth saving, the insides and edges of the floor board, chambers, queen excluder and cover board should be singed with a blow-lamp.

Most beekeepers will have some form of Insurance or Compensation Scheme to cater for such eventualities, so it is important to have documentation completed at the time if a claim for loss is to be made.

Varroatosis. The parasitic mite of the honey-bee, Varroa Jacobsoni, was first discovered by an entomologist named Oudemans on the Island of Java in 1904. The mite was found on the Asiatic bee Apis Cerana which appeared to co-exist with the parasite without causing noticeable loss to the colony. After the second world war, colonies of European honey-bees were introduced to the far-East and they surpassed the honey-gathering capabilities of the native Cerana bees. Unfortunately around the early nineteen-sixties, the Varroa mites began to parasitise the European bee-colonies and some of these affected bees were transported to different parts of the world. The two main sources of invasion to Europe came from Manchuria through Rusia and as a direct importation from Pakistan to West Germany. Since then Varroa has spread to almost every country in the world. At time of writing, countries which report freedom from the parasite include Australia, New Zealand, the Mainland of Scandinavia and the British Isles.

The Varroa female can lay up to seven eggs alongside a developing bee larva just before it is sealed over. The eggs hatch within a few hours into nymphs which feed on the blood of the bee-larva and later pupa. When the bee hatches, she is often deformed because of the parasitising. The released, mature mites can then attach themselves to adult bees, burrowing in between the abdominal segments where they again feed on the bees' blood. The mites are very difficult to detect at this stage and they can be carried by the flying bees to other hives or apiaries where they can start-up a new centre of pestilence.

To date there is no known cure for the condition although it is possible to keep Varroa-infested colonies alive by periodic applications of various chemicals coupled to manipulation and destruction of brood combs - particularly those containing drone brood. Without treatment, colonies of European honey-bees generally succumb within four years of the initial contamination.

It may be possible to contain an initial outbreak of Varroatosis in a previously unaffected country if it is detected early enough and the authorities pursue a vigorous destruction-policy with alacrity. The female Varroa mite is about the size of a small pin-head and is oval-shaped like a crab. It could be confused with a specimen of Braula. On close examination however, it will be seen that the Braula is round in shape and being an insect has only six legs whereas the Varroa is a mite, and like the rest of the members of the Arachnida class, it has eight legs *(Fig. 214)*.

The presence of Varroa may be detected by placing paper "hive inserts" on he floor boards of stocks then smoking the bees from the top with various fumigants - including tobacco smoke. The debris collected on the inserts is then subjected to close examination.

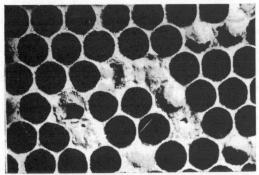

Fig. 201. Appearance of cells affected by American Foul Brood (Bacillus Larvae).

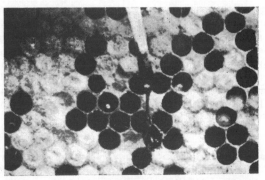

Fik. 202. The Ropiness Test of cell contents with match stick denotes A.F.B. present.

Fig. 203. Robbing bees attacking stock affected by A.F.B. Infected honey can be taken back to healthy stock and spread the disease.

Fig. 204. An old tin containing traces of honey from ur-known source being cleaned by bees. A.F.B. spores might be present.

Fig. 205. Sales of second-hand equipment should be treated with suspicion.

Fig. 206. Destroying infected stock. When bees have stopped flying, a petrol rag is used to seal up entrance.

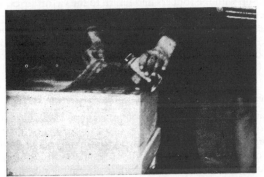

Fig. 207. A pint of petrol poured on top of colony quickly kills bees before destruction by fire.

Fig. 208. Applying sulphathiazol by dusting method.

71

Sac Brood. This malady is caused by a virus. The remains of the dead larva are described as being watery and contained in the outer skin which has a tough texture. The dead larva can be easily removed from its cell in one piece, as can the later dried-up scale which turns upward at the cell-mouth and resembles a Chinese slipper in form. Sac brood usually appears in early summer but disappers of its own accord later on. There is no recognised treatment except to re-queen from healthy stock in severe and persistent cases.

Shrimp Brood. As far as is known, this condition has not yet been described. During the months of June in 1957 and 1962 and early July 1975, there were heavy death rates amongst sealed-brood in hundreds of apiaries throughout the East of Scotland. The worst colonies had over a third of the sealed-brood affected all of which had died at the 13th or 14th day stage of development, having the body segments formed and the pigmentation of the eyes just starting. The dead pupae were quite firm - almost crisp, and were reminiscent of the consistency and appearance of small, freshly-cooked, peeled shrimps. The affected cells were scattered about in random fashion some being next to normal pupae of the same age. In all cases, the malady cleared up within a three-week period of the onset of the condition but on observing this in their apiaries, many beekeepers became worried because the initial appearance with dark and sometimes perforated cell-cappings, resembled that of American foul brood.

The outbreaks always followed a poor heather season the year before and it is interesting to record that not one case of the malady was seen amongst thousands of stock-inspections during the intervening years.

ADULT BEE MALADIES

Adult bees are subject to a great variety of diseases, but again, locality and climatic conditions have influence in their distribution. The race or strain of the bee colonies also affects the development of some of these diseases.

Acarine (Acarapis woodi)

Acarine is caused by a microscopic mite, which is a parasite frequenting the breathing tubes or tracheae of the adult bee. Migrating mites within the hive are able to enter the large anterior spiracle, or breathing orifice, of young adult bees up to nine days old. Here the mites establish a colony *(Fig. 210)* and feed on the tracheal blood and tissues, causing damage to and eventual death of the unfortunate hosts. The first sign presented to the beekeeper once acarine is firmly established in a colony, is a number of crawling bees, which often huddle together in small groups outside the hive. Many of these bees appear unable to fly and often display the characteristic "K" wings caused by partial paralysis of the wing muscles. *(Fig. 209)*. Unfortunately, by the time a colony shows such outward signs of infection, much damage would have already been done, many of the bees, although not yet paralysed, being already affected, with consequent shortening of their lives.

Acarine was first recognised as a malady of bees on the Isle of Wight during 1905 and when it appeared on the English mainland four years later, it was given the name "Isle of Wight Disease". The parasite spread northwards into Scotland and at the time the cause of the malady was not known. In 1919, a team led by Dr J Rennie and partly financed by A H E Wood, first discovered the mite in the tracheae of a bee at Aberdeen University. Acarine caused extensive damage to bee colonies in Scotland during the nineteen-twenties but all the native-type bees were not annihilated. It is true that many

beekeepers lost their entire apiaries at the time and that some of them re-stocked their hives with imported bees at later dates. Many others however, re-stocked with bees from neighbouring apiaries or from other sources within Scotland. A number of beekeepers had only some of their stocks or apiaries affected and they replenished their losses with their own bees taken from apiaries located elsewhere.

During the fifties, acarine still gave cause for concern but by regular sampling and early diagnosing, most affected colonies of native-type bees responded to treatment and appeared to be parasite-free within two years of the first recognition. Imported bees, mainly of Italian and Caucasian races however, once diagnosed as having acarine present and being given the standard treatment, seldom responded and generally succumbed during the second year of infestation.

Since the early sixties and up to the eighties, the incidence of acarine has been very slight in Scotland. It is suggested that either the mite has changed in character - maybe reverting to its role as an external parasite, or perhaps the race or strains of native-type bee now predominant in Scotland have developed a degree of tolerance or immunity to the attacks of the mite.

Precautions

So far, the only means of ascertaining if acarine is present in a colony, is by taking a sample of bees and subjecting them individually to dissection *(Figs. 211-212)*. Between 20 and 30 live bees are taken from each stock either from the entrance or the cover board of the hive, by scooping them up in partially-open match-boxes, each numbered according to the number or distinguishing-mark on the hive. No food should be included as this may render the sample into a sticky mess which makes later examination difficult.

Acarine can be spread between stocks and apiaries by drifting bees. Bee-stocks moved into orchards for early pollination services, and to the heather later in the year, are particularly at risk, because of the colder weather and the fact that bees damaged by acarine, are more likely to drift into strange hives than are healthy ones. The introduction of swarms from unknown sources may well be a vehicle for introducing acarine into otherwise healthy apiaries. Stray swarms should be isolated well away from the rest of the apiary until samples of bees from them have been examined and reported on.

When robbing occurs, the bees in the robbed colony often join-up with the robbers and return to the victor' hives, where they are generally accepted. A colony weakened by acarine and consequently prone to being robbed, can be another method of spread. Queen bees can also be affected so the introduction of queens from dubious sources should be avoided.

Treatment

If acarine is found by microscopic examination to have spread to over 50 per cent of the bees in a colony, it is normally not worth the bother of attempting to treat it; the risk of spreading by drifting is too great - besides it would be doubtful if such a colony would survive even with treatment. Combs from such colonies however are perfectly safe to use at a later date. The adult bees can be killed by using a little petrol or chloroform as if for A.F.B. destruction.

When acarine is found to be present to a lesser degree, the colony can be treated in late autumn or early spring when little or no brood is present, with the original Frow's mixture, (2 parts petrol, 2 parts nitrobenzene and 1 part safrol oil, all by volume.) Nitrobenzene is the active ingredient and some prefer to use this on its own. A dose of between a teaspoonful and a tablespoonful of the chemical, depending on the coverage of bees in the colony, is poured onto a small piece of absorbent material such as felt, whch is placed either on the brood-chamber, frame-tops or on the hive floor-board.

Hive entrances should be restricted to half an inch or so to discourage robbing as the fumes of the chemical masks colony odour and render the guard bees lethargic. Use perforated-zinc to allow ventilation.

During the active season, April till October, the use of dimite or chlorebenzilat, prepared under the trade names of "P.K." and "Folbex" in the form of impregnated paper strips, prove most satisfactory. When bees have ceased flying for the day, a Folbex strip is ignited and suspended by a wire, either in a space made by removing a comb from the hive, or by adding an empty super over the frame tops. The entrance is closed and the roof replaced to prevent escape of the fumes for about half an hour. This treatment is repeated at weekly intervals over a period until sampling shows the infestation has cleared.

Nosema (Nosema apis)

Nosema is a disease which in some seasons causes concern, especially amongst large-scale beekeepers, the causative agent being a parasitic protozoa which attacks the cells of the mid gut of adult bees. Nosema spores are ingested into the bee's stomach where they develop into the active form and within a week the parasitised cells burst and release a vast number of newly-formed spores, which are discharged in the faeces of infected bees. Bees usually defecate outwith the hive, but if they are prevented from doing so, such as during a prolonged spell of cold weather when flying is impossible, excreta may be voided over the combs. (Fig.213). As other bees attempt to clean up this waste matter, they in turn become infected and so the disease spreads. A colony with a mild attack of nosema may recover during the summer, as infected bees are able to void excreta, or die away from the hive. There is the risk, however, of spores left becoming a source of infection the following winter. It will be seen that climatic conditions regulate the degree of infection to a greater extent and some over-sheltered apiary are particularly conducive to its spread.

Outward signs of nosema are difficult to observe, for althoughs staining of combs sometimes occurs and bees may be seen to crawl feebly from the hive, these are not infallible guides. Frequently no outward signs are visible until well into spring, when a colony may dwindle through no apparent reason. The only satisfactory test which can be applied to a stock to determine if nosema is present, is again by sampling and microscopic examination. Bees are usually sampled for acarine and nosema at the same time, the examination for both diseases being conducted on the same bees.

Nosema can be introduced to an apiary by infected combs or bees, but it is again suggested that this disease is present in many colonies and only becomes troublesome under endemic conditions.

Treatment

Fortunately the spores of nosema are readily destroyed, but in order to do so, material for treatment must first of all be cleared of bees. Providing a colony is reasonably strong in early summer, the following treatment often proves satisfactory.

The queen is removed on a comb of brood which is marked with a drawing pin and placed in a new brood chamber filled with clean combs. This new chamber is now placed over a queen excluder above the original brood chamber, the combs of which having been crowded together to fill up the space left by the removal of the marked combs. After a week, a new brood nest should be established in the new top chamber and the original marked comb is now returned to the bottom chamber, the space left by this operation being filled with a further clean comb. Three weeks afterwards all brood should have hatched in the bottom chamber, then these old, empty combs are shaken free of bees and can be treated along with the original floor board, chamber, queen excluder and cover board. A new brood nest has been created in the fresh brood chamber which is now placed on a clean floor board and given a fresh queen excluder and cover board.

Felt pads approximately six inches square are saturated in an 80 per cent concentration of acetic acid and sandwiched between chambers of combs or other material to be treated and the piles of equipment rendered air-tight as far as possible (Figs. 215-216). The fumigation treatment is carried out for one week, after which the material is aired for at least a further seven days. If a stack is built on a screen board set on four bricks and another screen board placed on top, ventilation will be assured and robber bees excluded. If combs are completely empty of stores, formalin can be used in place of acetic acid.

Another form of control can be used on nosema when present in a colony. This is by attacking the protozoa with a drug while still in the stomach of the bee. This drug, known by the trade name of "Fumidil B", is fed to a stock in syrup or candy and appears most effective when the disease would be at its height, that is in spring. Unfortunately Fumidil B is reported not to remain stable in honey over long periods so it is unlikely to effect a complete cure within a season, as spores deposited on combs would be unaffected.

Amoeba Disease (Malpighamoeba mellifica)

This disease is caused by a protozoa which infests the malpighiantubules (part of the excretary system in insects), but is not so common nor devasting as nosema. Fumigation with acetic acid, as for nosema is the recognised treatment for stocks suffering from it.

Septicaemia (Bacillus apisepticus)

Septicaemia is a little-known disease which attacks the blood of the bee and can cause death. It is not considered a major malady and no cure has been devised.

Paralysis

Affected bees have a dark, shiny appearance and look slightly smaller than normal bees. This appearance is due to loss of body hair and affected bees can be seen struggling with healthy ones at the hive entrance. (Fig. 217). This activity, easily confused with robbing, can be confirmed on examining the interior of the stock, for if paralysis is present it can be detected on bees within the hive as well as at the entrance. There appears to be three forms of paralysis; chemical, which has been discussed; a virus about which little is known; and an inherent fault in the queen, thought by some to be caused by too-close inbreeding. Much can be done to prevent the spread of paralysis of the virus form by careful isolation of infected stocks and again, the set-up of an apiary to discourage drifting plays a part in maintaining the health of the colonies. Where a faulty queen is suspected, re-queening with a young queen of a vigorous strain is the solution.

Bee Louse (Braula coeca)

There exists a minute, wingless fly, red in colour, which makes its home inside a bee colony and is given the unflattering name of Bee Louse, or Blind Louse, by beekeepers. This fly is not a parasite in the sense that unlike the flea or louse on the human body, it does not feed on the blood of its host. Instead, it finds its way to the mouthparts of a feeding bee and sucks the mixture of honey and saliva exuded. (Fig. 219).

When present in a colony, braula are invariably found on the queen bee, but it is not homage to royalty which is being paid; it is simply that the queen is fed more lavishly and these little

Fig. 209. Acarine (Acarapis Woodi) infected bees inactive at hive entrance and forming small clusters (Photo MAFF)

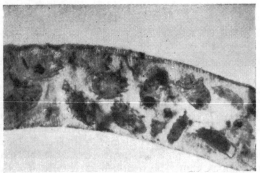

Fig. 210. Acarine. Infected Trachea, mites are plainly visible. (Photo MAFF)

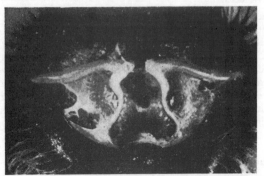

Fig. 211. Acarine disected bee. Healthy Trachae have pearly white appearance. (Photo MAFF)

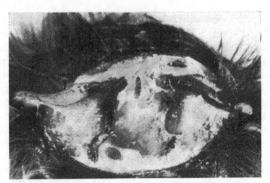

Fig. 212. Acarine. Infected Trachae show black patches due to the presecne of mites.
(Photo MAFF)

Fig. 213. Frame tops badly stained in stock infected with Nosema (Nosema Apis).

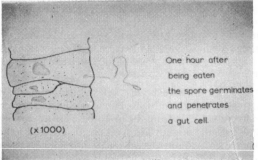

One hour after being eaten the spore germinates and penetrates a gut cell.

(x 1000)

Fig. 214. The Nosema spores germinate and attack the stomach cells. Within a week many other will form. (Photo MAFF)

Fig. 215. Fumigating brood chambers. Glacial acetic acid 80% is used to soak absorbent pads.

Fig. 216. Chambers are stacked with pads interspersed. Fumigation continues for a week then chambers thoroughly aired before use.

Lazareths of the hive congregate where the crumbs fall in greater profusion. Braula seldom cause great concern to bees, but where section honey is produced, the tunnelling of the braula larvae causes vein-like markings on the face of the cappings which detracts from the appearance of the finished product. *(Fig. 220).*

To eliminate this pest, it is common practice to lay a sheet of newspaper on the hive floor then apply fairly heavy puffs of tobacco smoke burnt in the smoker at intervals for about ten minutes before removing the paper with the dead or senseless braula and destroying it. The application of other chemicals including powdered camphor, has been tried with varying success. Phenothiazine has recently proved very satisfactory in the control of Braula. Two or three grams are burned along with smoker fuel and weekly applications given until the infestation has cleared up.

Wax Moths

The larvae of wax moths can, in some circumstances, cause vast damage to combs. *(Fig. 223).* The species which are generally blamed for this are the Greater Wax Moth (Galleria mellorella) and the Lesser Wax Moth (Achroia grisella), but the various species of clothes moths can also devastate combs. Normally damage is restricted to weak stocks, empty hives containing combs but particularly stored combs. If apiary sites and storage accommodation are kept clean and free from scattered, odd pieces of comb which afford breeding facilities for moths and if precautions are taken when storing combs, much will have been done to prevent later damage.

Some beekeepers prefer to store their combs "wet" from the extractor, as the presence of sticky surfaces deters the unwanted attentions of moths. This "wet" condition does not last indefinitely, besides being a messy procedure, and combs may be attacked should they be stored for a period over a few years. Wrapping each super in newspaper prevents the admission of egg-laying adult moths, but such labour is tedious and time-wasting. Perhaps the simplest method is to stack the supers or brood chambers of combs in piles and insert pieces of cardboard, on which is placed about half an ounce of P.D.B. (paradichlorobenzine) crystals, at intervals of three to four supers apart. The top and bottom of each pile is sealed with spare cover boards. Combs so stored should be thoroughly ventilated for several weeks before use in stocks.

In severe cases of infection, combs can be fumigated with acetic acid in the same manner as for nosema fumigation.

Wasps

Wasps are beneficial insects throughout the spring and summer months, but towards autumn, marauding hordes from the partially deserted nests can prove quite a menace to honey bee colonies, as they seek to plunder the honey stores, killing many bees in the process. Open lemonade bottles, a quarter filled with water, to which has been added a few spoonfuls of raspberry jam, make excellent traps and do not appear to attract honey bees. These can be scattered around the apiary and empted periodically as required. If a wasp nest is located - empty hives are frequently chosen *(Fig. 224)* it can usually be destroyed quite easily by introducing some suitable insecticide into it. It is advisable to wear protective clothing and a bee veil.

Birds

In some parts the attentions of the Green Woodpecker (Gecinus vinidis) cause much concern during severe winters, for not only are colonies of bees depleted or decimated, but serious damage to hive parts often results. *(Fig. 218).* At time of writing the Green Woodpecker is a protected bird and to destroy them would incur the wrath of the law, but a remedy can be effected by screening hives in apiaries likely to be attacked with wire or strawberry netting.

In winter and early spring some smaller species of birds, particularly the Tit family, prey on bees at the hive entrances. It is amusing to watch their antics as they frequently peck at the entrances of a hive until an inquisitive bee emerges and is speedily plucked up and devoured. A certain amount of bees are lost in this way, but the problem is seldom serious enough to warrant a remedy. If a stock dies of starvation, its combs are readily cleared of freshly dead bees if they are put in a position accessible to these birds during cold winter weather.

Mice

The bee colony forms its winter cluster and during frosty weather is unlikely to break it without loss of bees through chilling. At this stage, if ready access is available mice may enter a hive unchallenged and within a few weeks devastate the whole colony *(Fig. 222).*

The common house mouse and the harvest mouse are sometimes found in bee hives, but the chief offender in this country appears to be the long-tailed field mouse. (Apodemus sylvaticus). This elegant little gentleman with his beautiful reddish-brown coat and white under-part, is ever-anxious to repair to the cosy, well victualled residence afforded by a hive, there to dine sumptuously and while away the dark winter days with his harem of two females. On entering the hive, mice commence feeding on the pollen stores, following with honey, then by way of a dessert, finish off the banquet with parts of the bees themselves, the hard, indigestible parts of which are neatly nibbled off and left in tidy heaps. Although the mice may not complete their menu, appropriation of the stores may result in the colony dying from starvation.

The death of the colony is not the beekeeper's only loss. The combs in such a hive are generally eaten through the centres and the accumulation of nibbled comb and mice excreta on the floor board starts to decay. Bees often shun combs once they have been tainted by the odour of mice. The first indication of the unwelcome visitors is the presence of nibbled pieces of comb and mice excreta visible at the entrances *(Fig. 221).* Occasionally bees themselves strew pieces of comb over the entrances, especially where granulated stores are present, but these are much smaller and more regular than that damaged by mice. It is as well, however, to check up on a hive which shows any such signs.

Prevention is simple. In late autumn before night frosts set in, hives must be made mouse-proof. Quarter inch (6 mm) entrances form a barrier to mice, but on occasion the wood immediately above the entrance has been gnawed away to effect a passage. There are various methods of reducing entrances to exclude mice. A piece of zinc queen excluder can be fixed with drawing pins so that it covers the entire entrance, but has the disadvantage of tending to clog the entrance as comb capping and dead bees cannot be ejected. This debris may pile up against the queen excluder and interfere with ventilation. A complete queen excluder can be used in single-walled and in some double-walled hives by placing it immediately over the floor board. Wire excluders are best, for zinc ones tend to sag in the middle. Although this method is satisfactory in that it forms an effective mouse guard, it once again tends to impede ventilation and the queen excluders require a great deal of cleaning when removed.

A simple method is effected by cutting or breaking off by repeated bending, old, zinc queen excluder or perforated zinc, into strips approximately two inches broad and sufficiently long to cover the entrance of the hive. Two slips of wood are cut, slightly less than a quarter inch (6mm) thick and these are inserted into each corner of the floor board so that they project from the body of the hive. The strip of queen excluder is then placed over the entrance so that it rests on the wood slips and firmly fixed in position with three drawing pins. The slips are removed, leaving an entrance slightly less than a quarter of an inch (6 mm) without impeding ventilation and, what is particularly useful in an out apiary, the excluder may

Fig. 217 *Paralysis is often confused with robbing.*

Fig 218 *Damage done to hive by Green Woodpecker.*

Fig. 219 *Bee Louse (Braula Coeca) on Thorax of Worker Bee.*

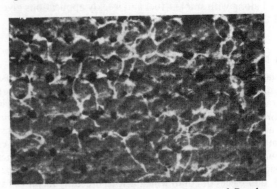

Fig. 220 *Tunnelling in Cappings by Larvae of Braula. (Photo M. Robb.)*

Fig. 221 *Debris at hive entrance indicates that mice are present.*

Fig. 222 *Damage Done to combs by mice. The bee colony was also killed.*

Fig. 223 *Comb badly attacked by wax moth.*

Fig. 224 *A wasps' nest found inside a bee hive attached to comb. Wasps can be troublesome at the end of summer.*

76

be left in position till well on in the summer without hindering flying bees.

If mice are present, immediate action is advisable. It is possible during cold weather to look down between the frames after gently removing the roof and cover, when frequently the mice or their nest can be seen. The brood chamber should then be lifted on to the inverted roof, care being taken not to disturb the cluster of bees, and the floor board cleaned. The damaged comb is now removed; the mice generally endeavour to escape at this stage and if a deep roof is used, are effectively trapped as they fall into it and can be despatched with a hive tool. Once all the mice are expelled, the hive should be reassembled and the damaged combs replaced with either combs of stores or drawn comb, to prevent the risk of brace comb being built in the spring. A hive which has been so treated must be doubly protected against another invasion, for even if the mice in the hive have been accounted for, the scent left is apt to encourage other intruders.

Supers stored in houses or sheds should also be well protected, a simple method being to pile the supers on top of a queen excluder and to place a queen excluder on the top of the pile.

Homo Sapiens

It may well be, dear reader, that after perusing the foregoing chapter, hands are thrown up in despair and dark thoughts assail the mind that to keep bees free from pests and disease is a remote possibility. Let us hasten to remember however, that the bee colony is much older than man himself and has existed alongside these parasitical organisms over countless centuries. Modern methods of agriculture, horticulture, forestry and beekeeping tend to concenrate cropping and husbandry into congested areas and thereby create artificial or rather new conditions. This can have and has had a marked influence on the spread and retention of many diseases, but by careful observation, early diagnosing and modern treatment, these can be kept in check to a high degree.

It is well to bear in mind, however, the last and probably the most dangerous potential enemy of bees - that of the beekeeper himself. The careless or avaricious beekeeper can spread disease more so than by any natural means; he can create havoc in an apiary through mismanagement; he can, by opposing Nature, prevent natural selection of the fittest; and by robbing colonies over-much of their hard-won stores, he can leave them to perish from starvation.

Those who would profit by the keeping of the honey bee must ever be prepared to emulate some of the diligence and cleanliness shown by their tiny, yet industrious, servants.